Post War Land Drainage

William. R. Alderson

Post War Land Drainage

William. R. Alderson

Japonica Press

ISBN: 978-1-90-468637-8

A catalogue record for this book is available from the British
Library

Published by
Japonica Press
Low Green Farm, Hutton, Driffield,
East Yorkshire YO25 9PX
United Kingdom

Contents

Mother and Father at a wedding in 1968.

Acknowledgements

I am extremely grateful to those who have helped me compose
this book:

Past employees
Les Helme, Dennis Cloughton and Ron Snaith

Family members
Alf Alderson, Donald and Jane Alderson, Anne Alderson and
Jemma Alderson

And those who have allowed me to use their photographs given
advice, or helped in any other way
David Caley
Neil Roberts
Roger Wilkinson
Andy Crawshaw
The Museum of English Rural Life
David Armitage, of York Handmade, formerly Alne Brick Co
Lol Charlton, of Swale and Ure Drainage Board
Eric Clayton, of E.A. Clayton Limited
David Coxon, of Coxon Brothers
Sam Turner & Sons Limited
Geoff Nichols, for advice on Ruston Bucyrus

David Weedon, of Transport Fabrications Limited, for advice on
Priestman Brothers
Pam Harlow and Graham Towndrow, of the Nuffield Tractor Club
Caroline Timson, for Dinkum Digger photographs

Author's Note

I have used the imperial units that were in use at the time: feet
and inches, which most people will still be familiar with, but
also chains. A chain is the length of a cricket pitch, which, as
every schoolboy knows, is 22 yards, or approximately 20 metres.
A chain measure was exactly that: a chain measuring 22 yards
in length divided into 100 links. Some old legal documents
use chains and links when describing length of roads or road
frontage of a property. A chain also has connections with acres,
as 10 square chains, or 4,840 square yards, equate to 1 acre.
Everything to do with land drainage was measured in chains,
from the size of a scheme to the daily output of a machine.

A measuring chain, 22 yards
long, made up of 100 links.

In the early years we used a measuring chain when setting drains
out. After the first lateral had been positioned it was important
that subsequent ones were laid parallel to it. We used the chain to
measure from one set of sight poles to the next. If draining at 22-
yard spaces, the full chain was used. We then had a piece of string
through a link at the 18-yard mark if that width was required.
It was a fairly durable thing and could be pulled about through
water and mud without any harmful effects, which could not be
said for the alternative – the measuring tape.

Introduction

This book follows on from my previous one entitled *Threshing Days: A Story of Farming in the North Riding*. That book followed the business started by my late father, William Oswald Alderson (W.O.), in the late 1930s, to the final days of threshing in 1971. This new book covers the period from 1960 to 1972, which saw the end of threshing and the start of land drainage, and the gradual build-up of those activities through those 12 years. The year 1972 was the point in time when I left the family business, bought some of the general contracting equipment and developed my own business.

These are my recollections of the development of the business from a small, mainly threshing contracting business in the 1950s to a medium sized land drainage business by the early 1970s. There is a continuous story that runs all the way through the book, and interjected are chapters on:

The hydraulic tractor-mounted excavator
The rotary trench digger
A brief history of land drainage
Grant-aided schemes
Rope-operated excavators
Rillington Depot
And a final postscript.

Foreword

Ever since the Enclosure Act, landowners and farmers have tried to harness nature, to help them improve both the land and the yields from that land.

One of the most cost effective methods of land improvement was by drainage, a practice which rapidly evolved and developed with the industrial revolution, and the twentieth century's technological advances.

Back in my childhood in the early 1960's, I became fascinated by trenching machines and excavators, the primary tools of the drainage contractor, which were bought, sold, repaired and serviced by my father's company. At the same time, William Alderson was using and operating such machinery commercially, working for his father's company. Our fathers knew each other well, and did much business together.

The name of W O Alderson was well known and respected in North East England, particularly in Yorkshire and Co Durham. Customers knew that, if the contract was placed with 'W O', the job would be carried out efficiently, speedily, with minimum disruption and with maximum attention to detail. Other drainage contractors could look at a job completed by one of W O's teams, and see for themselves the standard to which they had to aspire, in order to compete.

Thus William has excellent credentials to bring to life the story of his introduction to drainage contracting, and the subsequent growth, expansion and success of the family company.

But over and above, William has combined this fascinating story with a highly detailed reference guide to the tools, equipment, duties and responsibilities of a drainage contractor. He discusses in depth, the advantages and drawbacks of different makes and models of machines and equipment, the correct method and procedure to follow when undertaking a project, and the correct ongoing management of the scheme by the farmer or landowner, once the contractor has completed the installation, and left the site.

This book is a fascinating read for the historian, the engineer, the farmer and landowner, and indeed for anyone with an interest in the life, history and practices of the countryside.

David Caley
Keyingham, East Yorkshire
July 2015

And so to the Story

The mainstay of the business from 1942 had been threshing, rising to three sets in the early 1950s. (A threshing set comprises one threshing machine, one tractor, possibly a baler or trusser, and two men.) In 1954, this was reduced to two sets and a noticeable decline of work was apparent as more and more farmers turned to the combine harvester. We had always done a certain amount of ploughing; a rotavator was bought in 1954 and we did a modest amount of corn drilling. A Ransomes Cropguard sprayer was used from 1952, but in those days this was only a short season, with only a spring herbicide being used. This was a product called Shell M, which was basically MCPA, which we bought in 40-gallon barrels.

From 1954 we had a grass mower, a pick-up baler, which we increased to two by the late 1950s. Two binders were used in the early fifties. This reduced to one in 1953, and by the end of the decade this machine was almost redundant. We ran a combine from 1954 onwards, a Massey Harris 8-foot 6-inch cut bagger version. With only a few other sundry activities, this was the total of our contracting business in the 1950s.

As the threshing declined in the late 1950s we needed another enterprise to take its place. We considered taking on other things under the heading of 'general contracting'; muck spreading, forage harvesting and potato harvesting were all thought of but rejected. These were only short, seasonal activities when what we needed was a job to last the whole of the winter at least, and, if possible, extending into the summer months as well.

W.O. was an active member of the National Association of Agricultural Contractors (NAAC), not only at local level but at national level as well. Meetings in London brought him into contact with contractors from all over the country, and from the exchange of views that went on he was able to learn from some of their experiences. From this he became more and more interested in land drainage in some form or another as a replacement for threshing.

During the Second World War the government had set up the War Agricultural Executive Committee, which became shortened to War Ag. This was set up under the umbrella of the Ministry of Agriculture Fisheries and Food, and their remit was to help increase home produced food. As well as offering a comprehensive general contracting service they also carried out scrub clearance, ditching and drainage work. When the war was over they carried on for some years, but their instructions in peacetime were that as soon as private contractors were able to take on the work, they would then cease trading. By the early 1950s their general contracting was reducing rapidly, with many of their depots being closed. Sales of War Ag equipment were regular occurrences as their operations were scaled back. Here in the North Riding of Yorkshire all their outlying depots were closed by 1955, from when on their sole activities were land drainage, ditching and scrub clearance, which was then all run from their central depot in Northallerton.

From his contacts through the NAAC, W.O. knew that the War Ag's drainage activities were not going to be a long-lasting business. The other factor that came into his thinking was that approved drainage schemes qualified for a 50 per cent government grant, so that farmers would be more likely to have this work done if they perceived a need. Surveys were published from time to time proclaiming how many millions of acres would benefit from draining, and the rate at which it was being done at that time was not keeping pace with the deterioration in existing systems.

The question that still remained was what type of machine to buy in order to start us off? Most of the straightforward land drainage was being done by small rotary wheel trench

The Ransomes mounted mole drainer.

diggers, which used farm tractors for their power source, but they were, of course, restricted to that type of work only. The North Riding War Ag was using two Howard rotary trenchers as well as Priestman Wolf excavators. The Priestmans were capable of field drainage, ditch cleaning and a multitude of other earth-moving duties. The other machine that some private contractors were using by the late 1950s was the hydraulic tractor-mounted digger/loader combination. The advantage of this type of machine was that it could dig drainage trenches and clean ditches out, as well as having a loader to handle aggregate or backfill trenches.

Whichever of these options was chosen it would need a considerable amount of capital. Much of the field drainage by this time had gravel backfill, requiring, in addition to the machine, a side discharge trailer and a loader, which at that time we did not have. Some means of backfilling the spoil would be needed, as well as all the hand tools and levels, all of which would have to be bought. The Howard trenchers at this time were all fitted with Rotaped tracks and steel front wheels, so some form of low loading trailer would be needed for transport. The only thing we did have was a Ransomes mole drainer.

This was a tractor-mounted one that could get down to 24 inches deep (although 18-21 inches was more usual), but even at that depth, two Fordson Majors were needed, or the one on the mole drainer and a winch in front pulling it along, particularly at the greater depths.

In the summer of 1960 the decision was made and a second-hand hydraulic excavator was bought. It was a 1955 Dinkum Digger, manufactured by Whitlock Brothers from Great Yeldham.

There is a saying in current use that is, "It was a steep learning curve"; well, that summed up our first months and years in land drainage.

The Hydraulic Tractor-Mounted Excavator

The hydraulic back actor first appeared in 1953/4. The first make on the British market was the Whitlock Dinkum Digger, then, in the following year, the first JCB was announced. These were followed soon after by a machine from Steel Fabricators of Cardiff known as the Shawnee Scout.

John Allen & Sons of Oxford marketed the Allen Tractor Operated Shovel or 'ATOS' machine, which was not mounted to the tractor as such, but was a trailed machine on two wheels and a drawbar. The hydraulic pump was mounted on the machine and driven by a shaft from the tractor's power take-off (PTO). This appeared to be a cheap alternative without disfiguring a tractor. I can remember being at a demonstration of this machine at which, with an experienced operator, it seemed to perform perfectly well, but in practice there were problems. It was a relatively light machine and being virtually free-standing was not very stable with a bucket of soil swinging from side to side. Some operators were injured when the thing overturned, trapping them in the process.

W & G (Challow) Limited was a small Bedfordshire firm that had originally specialised in horse-drawn wagons and carts. These developed into tractor-drawn trailers. We knew of them in the 1950s as makers of bale sledges, which were all-wooden affairs, towed behind the baler with a man riding on it stacking the bales. Their trailers became hydraulic tippers, which gave the firm experience of hydraulic rams and hoses.

The W & G land drainer, developed in the mid-fifties, at 2¾ tons was a much heavier machine than the Allen ATOS. It again was a trailed machine on two wheels connected to the tractor by the

An Allen ATOS at a vintage machinery show in New Zealand

The W & G land drainer at work running parallel to the ditch.

drawbar and its hydraulic pump driven by the tractor's PTO. This machine was designed as the hydraulic replacement for the dragline. The boom was telescopic, allowing the bucket 5 foot of movement. It could then be slid into a position outside the left-hand wheel, while a counterbalance weight at the right-hand side mounted on an arm moved in and out to counter the weight of the digging arm. The idea of this elaborate arrangement was to allow a tapered ditch-cleaning bucket to be drawn along a ditch with the machine standing close to it. It was an elaborate machine, with no fewer than seven hydraulic controls. It was advertised in the farming journals for several years in the late 1950s and early 1960s. It did win an RASE silver medal in 1957. I have no information as to how many were sold or how successful they proved to be in use, but I never knew of one in this area and they eventually disappeared from the scene.

The Dinkum Digger was developed in 1952 by Mr Robert Ewan, from Fife in Scotland, and built onto a Ferguson tractor. The manufacturing rights were then sold to the Whitlock Brothers of Great Yeldham. All digger manufacturers would be aware of the fact that a hydraulic ram is more powerful when extending than it is when contracting. The designers of the Dinkum knew this and constructed a trapezium arrangement for lifting the jib so that the lifting ram was pushing when lifting. Whitlock Brothers continued with this design until the end of production in the 1970s. The Mark I Dinkum was a light affair built by Mr Ewan on a Ferguson tractor; the Mark II, built in Essex, was a heavier machine built onto a Fordson Major tractor but still using the same basic principles. The Mark III was very similar, with only minor modifications. Our first machine was a Mark III, so I am able to give a full description of that particular model.

There were two frame members pivoted under the axle of the tractor and extended rearwards approximately 6 feet and outwards to the width of the tractor tyres. The central swivel post of the machine was mounted approximately halfway along these frame members. The tractor's lower hydraulic lift arms

The Mark I Dinkum Digger mounted on a Ferguson tractor.

The feet of the Mark I Dinkum Digger.

were utilised, with some links connected to these frame members at approximately the same point as to where the king post was mounted. So when travelling, the digger was lifted clear of the ground by the tractor lift arms. It was then lowered to the ground before digging commenced. There was a strut between the top link point of the tractor to the cross-member supporting the king post. On the Mark II this was a threaded rod with a wheel nut to lock it; on the Mark III this was a hydraulic ram that obtained its oil from the machine's oil reservoir, which was located along side the right-hand tractor mudguard. A wheel valve was deployed to keep it fully extended when digging. This ensured that one side foot could not leave the ground when a bucket of earth was swung to the other side. A sprag was located under the tractor, mounted on two struts pivoted again under the axle, with a length of heavy angle iron connecting the two and trailed on the ground. This would engage with the land and prevent the machine from moving backwards as the machine was digging. The 'top link' from the tractor's top link bracket to the top of the king post was made of two strips of steel, with a gap between through which a chain passed. This chain was attached to the sprag and used to hold it clear of the ground to allow reversing.

The Mark III Dinkum Digger.

The Dinkum Digger's trapezium lifting arrangement.

The digging mechanism became the conventional format, albeit with this Dinkum trapezium lift arrangement. It had four hydraulic levers, as had all diggers at this time, centrally mounted, and the tractor seat had a swivel fitted under it to allow the driver to swing round and face the digging operation. A cab was fitted that looked like the Winsam tractor cab of that time, but was, in fact, manufactured by Whitlock Brothers. It was similar to the farm tractor cabs but a rear window was fitted, which only came down to mudguard level. If working on a wet day, the driver's knees got wet. The slewing was accomplished by one double-acting ram that gave it 150 degrees of swing,

which was not enough to allow ditching work with a conventional ditching bucket. The hydraulic pump was mounted on the front casting of the tractor and driven from the front of the engine crank shaft.

These machines were built onto a standard Fordson Major tractor and used the tractor axles and wheels. The usual tractor bonnet was retained and the whole thing was painted in Fordson Major blue.

The wire rope slewing arrangement on the Dinkum Major.

Whitlock's did make a front-end loader to accompany the back actor, although our machine was fitted with a SkyHi loader. The Whitlock loader was of the high pivot type similar to the SkyHi, but it would always have hydraulic bucket tip, whereas the SkyHi had a manual bucket tip. Whitlock's own loader was powered by oil from the digger pump, while the SkyHi relied on the tractor's own hydraulics.

By 1958, Whitlock's had developed the Dinkum Major. It was sold alongside the Mark III for a short while before the Mark III was withdrawn from the market. It was a larger machine, which was attached rigidly to the tractor. It was still built onto a Fordson Major, which by now had become the Power Major. This model had its own fully enclosed cab and independent hydraulic stabilisers. A peculiarity of this machine that was retained by Whitlock's until they ceased trading was that the two short levers that activated the stabilisers worked opposite to those of all other manufacturers: pulling them extended the feet downwards and pushing them away retracted them. It still utilised the trapezium

lifting mechanism; the big difference was in the slewing device. Two single acting rams were laid longitudinally under the tractor with a length of wire rope from one ram passing around a pulley at the base of the king post and back to the other ram. The advantage of this system was that it gave in excess of 180 degrees of slew; the disadvantage was that the rope had to be kept tight and needed constant maintenance.

From 1961 to 1963, the Dinkum Super Major was on the market. It was essentially the same machine but with heavier steel used in the jib and the digging and lifting rams were increased in diameter. In 1963, Whitlock's replaced the Dinkum Super Major with the Dinkum 60 and 66. The number 60 referred to the back actor and 66 the front loader. The most noticeable change was the colour scheme; the Fordson blue gave way to industrial yellow, with a red cab. Whitlock's now made a heavier front axle with 9-inch wide front tyres, but the Fordson Major bonnet was still used. Otherwise, this machine remained as the earlier ones. In 1965, the Dinkum name was dropped and the new machines were simply known as Whitlocks: the 105 was the smallest, suitable for Ferguson or the small International tractors. The 205 and 305 were built onto the Ford 4000 and the 405 was on the Ford 5000. Many of their competitors were now offering a slide arrangement that enabled the king post to be moved to one side of the machine to allow working close to walls etc. Whitlock's developed a swinging arrangement not unlike a tractor's swinging drawbar: two box section beams were pivoted under the driving seat with the king post at the rear end of them. There were then three positions where they could be pinned. Machines with this arrangement were the 105, 305 and 405, while the 205 had the king post fixed in the central position. The wire rope slewing was discontinued and a system of swinging links was adopted. This still utilised two single acting rams but they were connected to either side of the king post by steel links about a foot long. This allowed one side to pull the digger unit into the 90 degree position while the other side would pivot around the base of the king post courtesy of the swinging link.

For the 1970's Whitlocks updated their excavator range into two models the 370 on a Ford 4000 tractor and the 570 on a Ford 5000 tractor. They were now painted orange and a Whitlock bonnet and nose cone replaced the Ford one.

This range of excavators continued in production until 1972 when, following the death of Mr Charlton Whitlock, the whole business was sold to the Hymac Co of Rymmny in South Wales. Hymacs were selling a range of tracked hydraulic excavators and after the Whitlock acquisition they continued to sell the same two tractor mounted machines. The trapezium lifting arrangement was discontinued it also had rails across behind the tractor wheels allowing the kingpost to be slid from side to side.

From the Whitlock 205/305 driver's instruction manual.

The Mark I JCB on a Fordson Major tractor.

Without doubt, Brittan, and probably the world's most successful tractor mounted excavator was the JCB. Joseph Cyril Bamford was an engineer who after the Second World War began making various implements and appliances for local farmers. By the late 1940's he was making a hydraulic tipping trailer, he then made a front end loader and by 1954 he had come up with the first hydraulic digging attachment to go on the rear of a tractor. This was painted orange and sold as a fitting for the Fordson Major tractor which retained its original colour, and the now familiar JCB logo was displayed on the jib.

These machines were of what became the conventional design with a jib lifted by a hydraulic ram, which in this case pulled to lift. The dipper arm was extended above the jib, allowing the digging ram to push to dig, and then a bucket crowd ram was located down the back of the dipper arm. Slewing was achieved by a rack and pinion system. A double acting hydraulic ram with piston rods protruding from both ends was positioned horizontally across the machine. A toothed rack was attached to the side of the hydraulic cylinder, and a 'pinion' was formed around the base of the swivel post. This ram traversed across the machine, swinging the jib as it did so. This was a very positive system of slewing and gave a full 180 degrees of slew. The subframe was lifted and lowered by a double acting ram powered by the digger's own hydraulics, which could apply sufficient down pressure onto the subframe to lift the tractor's back wheels clear of the ground. By the standards of the day, this was a big machine, with a maximum digging depth of 11 feet and an outreach of 15 feet, and bucket widths ranging from 18 to 48 inches.

JCB's rack and pinion slewing mechanism.

In 1955, they adopted the industrial yellow as their standard colour, with red wheels. This machine was known as the Mark I; it brought together all the JCB features, including a front-end loader, and fitted them around a Fordson Major tractor. For the front-end loader, hydraulic bucket crowd became a standard feature. In 1957, this was updated to the Hydra-Digger. This machine was quite a bit bigger than its predecessors and was the biggest tractor-mounted digger available at that time.

The digger driving position, in what was quite a roomy cab for that period, was positioned at the right-hand side when viewed from the rear of the machine. One thing the driver had to be wary of was that when lifting the digger to move forward, the rear-facing seat and controls were mounted on the digger mechanism, so that when lifting the digger, the driver's headroom reduced quite rapidly. In fact, a tall man was well advised to leave the seat first and then operate the lifting lever. The Hydra-Digger could dig down to a depth of 13 feet and had an outreach of 18 feet.

It was during the lifetime of the Hydra-Digger that JCB first introduced the two-lever control. The main four hydraulic levers were replaced by two, which now had crossover functions in addition to the normal back and forward movement. In the case of JCB, these movements were diagonal motions, unlike all other manufacturers, who went for straight north-south and east-west configurations when they adopted the two-lever control.

The JCB
Hydra digger.

The Hydra-Digger was replaced by the JCB 4 in 1959. This was of similar design although it was bigger and heavier still. The most noticeable change was to the cab. The previous one was similar to the tractor cabs of that era but the one fitted to the JCB 4 was a much larger and squarer affair, with loads of room to walk about in it. A similar method of stabilisation was used as on the earlier machines, but now there was an angle iron beam across under the subframe with the web down over, which engaged with the earth and made the machine very stable. On either end of this cross-beam were two extension pieces, which when not in use were fastened vertically, but could be pinned horizontally to give even greater stability. Or they could be pinned at a slight angle to keep the machine vertical on sloping ground. This machine was brutally strong and, in our view at the time, far too heavy for farm work. As it was mounted on a two-wheel drive tractor it often had difficulty moving itself around.

The JCB 4.

The JCB 3 was introduced in late 1961. This machine, although obviously smaller and lighter than the 4, had a similar external appearance, and was still mounted on the Fordson Major tractor, with the same size of tyre. It would dig to a depth of 11 feet and had an outreach of 15 feet 7 inches. A dipper extension of 2 feet was available, which increased both of those figures. The rack and pinion slewing was retained, although on this machine fully enclosed, and it gave a slewing range of 200 degrees. Nevertheless, there were some detailed changes that moved digger development on quite considerably. Running across and behind the tractor were rails that carried the king post. It could be locked in any position across these rails, allowing digging to be performed anywhere behind the tractor and right up to a wall, if necessary. These beams were connected vertically at either end by the stabilisers. These were made from a length of box section steel with a smaller section fitted inside, which could be raised and lowered hydraulically. To move the king post across the beams some clamps were released and, with the bucket fully swung to either right or left, bringing the bucket in would move the king post across the rails. It was now recommended for road transport that the king post be fully drawn to one side of the machine, and then the bucket swung across the back of the machine. The driving position was now in the centre of the machine and, as with the JCB 4, it was a roomy cab with no side door, the only access being over these cross-rails and in through the back.

The JCB 3.

The following year they marketed the JCB 1. This was a very small machine with a Petter twin-cylinder diesel engine. It did not have a front-end loader but a simple blade across the front, which with down pressure could be used to stabilise the machine. The driver had the benefit of the smaller but now familiar-looking JCB cab. It found a small market, mainly with local authorities. Indeed, it was given the nickname of the 'grave digger'. JCBs continued with their rack and pinion slewing arrangement right down to this small JCB 1. Machines with the sliding king post had a fully enclosed slewing system, although still a rack and pinion.

This was followed up by the JCB 2. This was of a similar construction to the 3, although quite a bit smaller. The significant difference was that it was the first JCB not mounted on a Fordson Major tractor; instead, a three cylinder Nuffield was used. This machine was available in two formats. The alternative to the standard design was the JCB 2B, on which the digging machine was easily detached from the tractor, leaving a manoeuvrable tractor loader machine.

The JCB 1, or 'grave digger', as it became known

The JCB 7 tracked machine.

In 1964, they made their first move into the tracked excavator market with the JCB 7. Several manufacturers were selling tracked hydraulic machines at this time and the JCB proved to be a worthy competitor. It was big, heavy and had its lifting ram under the jib pushing to lift. It had a Perkins six-cylinder engine and all-steel tracks, which were hydraulically driven and of the chain and bolt on grouser plate type.

In 1964, production of the Fordson Major tractor ceased, to be replaced by the Ford 4000 and 5000s. For some time, the people at JCB had been less than happy with the Fordson. There were several minor complaints but the biggest concern related to access to the tractor clutch. In the agricultural tractor form the Fordson Major was split to give access to the clutch, but this was not possible when fitted within the frame of a JCB. The only way of servicing the clutch was to remove the engine. On the Nuffield tractor the clutch could be accessed by removing the top of the clutch housing and not splitting the tractor. The new

The Shawnee Scout on a Fordson Major tractor, more often seen on a Ferguson 35.

Ford tractors had done nothing to alleviate this problem so JCB decided to change and use the skid form version of the Nuffield tractor instead. Joe Bamford, never one to let a publicity opportunity slip through his hands, had one of his machines dig a large hole; the last Fordson Major was lowered into it and buried.

As tracked machines became more widely accepted, the JCB 4 was phased out and production of wheeled machines was centred on the JCB 3. It was constantly updated as the 3C, 3CII, 3CX, etc. One thing that is certain is that it was probably the most successful wheeled digger of all time. In fact, the firm of JCB would go on to be one of this country's most successful manufacturing companies of the post-war era.

Steel Fabricators Limited (Cardiff) turned out the Shawnee range of diggers in the late 1950s. As their name implies,

these machines were from North American origins, with Steel Fabricators obtaining the manufacturing rights.

Their first machine built onto a Ferguson tractor was the Shawnee Scout. It was a lightweight machine of all-tubular construction with a peculiar digging action. Whereas most machines have the dipper arm extended above the jib with the digging ram pushing on the top of it, this one was different. The digging ram was laid along the jib pivoted at the far end of it and pushing a carriage along the jib towards the tractor. This carriage consisted of rollers top and bottom of the jib held in place by two pieces of plate, which then had two lengths of steel pivoted from these plates and connected to the bottom of the dipper arm above the bucket. In the digging mode the extending ram pushed this carriage along the jib, which in turn drew the bucket towards the operator.

The Shawnee Warrior.

By 1960, they had the Shawnee Warrior on the market, which was offered with either the Fordson Major or the Nuffield as its power source. This was a much more up-to-date machine, with the conventional digging arrangement. With the digging ram pushing against the extended dipper arm, the bucket crowd ram was located within the dipper arm. This machine had a maximum digging depth of 11 feet 9 inches and an outreach of 17 feet.

It had independent hydraulic stabilisers, which could be extended to be much wider than the tractor. It slewed through 180 degrees courtesy of a chain between two single acting hydraulic rams. These rams were positioned vertically either side of the driver's seat. The chain descended around idler sprockets and it then had a block that turned it through 90 degrees before going round a large sprocket at the bottom of the king post. It was complemented by the Shawnee special loader. The tractor's own front axle and bonnet were retained although the whole machine was finished in industrial yellow. The final touch was one of the most hideous cabs known to man. As somebody put it, "It looks like Ned's shed."

In the mid-1960s the Shawnee name was dropped and the replacement machines were known as SFs, the largest of which

was the SF180. This was similar to the Shawnee Warrior, but with a much squarer and more attractive cab and by now was fitted around a Ford 4000 tractor. They also made a range of smaller machines that were intended as three-point linkage attachments to farm tractors.

The SF 800 tractor attachment.

In 1959, a breath of fresh air swept through the excavator world with the introduction of the Massey Ferguson digger loader combination. It was everything that the JCB was not; it was fast, light and very manoeuvrable. Built around the industrial version of their 35 tractor, with an optional four-speed foot-operated torque converter, the standard gearbox model was designated the 203 and the torque converter model the 205. The digger was also available on their 65 model tractor, known as the 65S with standard transmission or 65R for torque converter models.

This machine was developed by the Davies Co in North America, who then sold the manufacturing rights to Massey Ferguson. It was manufactured both in North America and Great Britain. The British-built back actor was numbered the 710, following the MF practice of numbering everything they made in Great Britain commencing with a seven, and the loader was the 702. It was a conventional digging arrangement, with hydraulic stabilisers being of the telescopic box section type. The valve

The Massey Ferguson digger, with Peter Whitfield at the controls.

block with levers and the driver's seat were attached to the jib, directly above the king post, and the driving position swung in relation to the digging arm so that the driver always faced his work. It had vane pump slewing, which has since become the norm on British-built diggers. The king post supporting the digging arm was secured to the subframe by bolts in any one of three positions. It was quite an undertaking to change from one digging position to another, with jacks or lifting gear being needed. It could dig either centrally or to either side.

This machine did not lend itself to the fitting of a cab as the digging seat was a considerable way back from the tractor seat.

Some cab manufacturers tried by fitting two cabs, one for the digging position and one for the loading position, but this was not very satisfactory and most machines were used without cabs.

By 1964, the 710 digger had been superseded by the 220, the main difference being the fitting of cross-rails behind the tractor mudguards, allowing the digging arm to be slid across the machine into any one of five positions. To do this it was first necessary to loosen some clamping bolts, then pull the king post across with the bucket in the right-angle position and tighten the clamping bolts once more.

Two of Eric Clayton's Massey Ferguson machines laying a cable accross Whitby Harbour at low tide.

Eric Clayton, a drainage contractor from Stockton-on-Tees who ran four of these machines, modified one of them by moving the digger driving position much closer to the tractor. The seat was now fixed in position and an anchoring unit was located above the slewing motor so that the original MF hoses could be used, with some further ones made to go to the valve block. A Massey Ferguson sales representative looked at this conversion, took some photographs and away he went. Eric was astonished some weeks later when he received a sales leaflet from Massey Ferguson showing pictures of his modification and advising that this 'approved attachment' was available from E.A. Clayton. Winsam, the cab makers, looked at the machine and fairly quickly produced a cab that covered both driving positions. Eric received quite a few orders for this modification, which were made in his own workshop.

Massey Ferguson did not make this modification for the 220 machine before its replacement came along in 1971. This was the 50 series, on which the driver's digging position was fixed much closer to the tractor driving position, as on Eric Clayton's machine, so that one cab covered both positions.

With the arrival of the new Ford tractors in late 1964, and having lost the JCB contract, Ford quickly followed up with their own make of digger. This was known as the 13/6, a traditional style of machine with a big cab that had no door, the only access being through the open back. The stabilisers were of the pivoted swing down type, which most manufacturers had abandoned in favour of telescopic types. The machine had somewhat of an outdated look from the start but was nevertheless a good, solid and reliable performer. It was updated in the 1970s to the 550, and then the 555, and it was eventually incorporated into the Case/ New Holland range of excavators.

Eric Clayton's modification to one of his own machines.

The modified machine with Winsam cab fitted.

In the sixties and seventies there was a multitude of British manufactures or engineering firms turning out small hydraulic diggers aimed at farmers. These fitted to a farm tractor, usually on the three-point linkage, although some form of stabiliser would also be needed. In the 1950s, the firm of F.W. McConnel were selling their power arm. This was a tubular arm, carried on the three-point linkage, and extending to the right-hand side of the tractor, onto which a number of different attachments could be added. It could have a driven shaft up inside the tube or a pulley to the rear, with a flat belt taking power to the appliance. These attachments ranged from a sack lifter to a concrete mixer, with probably the most useful being a hedge cutter, which could be either finger bar or circular saw. In the early 1960s they developed a digger attachment for it. It simply had a dipper

Close-up of a new machine with the Clayton seating position.

arm on the end of the power arm, hydraulically powered, and another ram for bucket crowd. But there was no means of slewing it. It would be relatively successful at ditch cleaning with the tractor running parallel to the ditch. For trench digging work it operated as a normal digger, but when the bucket was full, the spoil was tipped out behind the tractor. There was then a blade fixed across the back of the tractor so that by reversing, this heap of spoil could be pushed out of the way of the next length of trench. The driver then had to manoeuvre the tractor sideways and back into line in order for the next length of trench to be dug. There were only a few of these about; it may have been useful for burying a sheep, but I cannot believe that anybody would seriously consider digging long stretches of trench with that machine.

McConnel later made a light digger with slewing facility that would have performed quite well on a limited scale. Probably the best of the crop of small diggers was that of Foster's, of North Cave, Humberside. It was a sensible looking machine of box section construction. It had all the sophistication of the larger machines, including hydraulic stabilisers, and a driver's seat mounted on the digger frame so that, as with the Massey Ferguson, the driver always faced his work. The hydraulic pump on these machines was on the digger frame and driven from the tractor's PTO shaft.

The Foster D2 digger.

The McConnel digging attachment for their power arm.

Back to the Story

The Mark III Dinkum was bought in mid-summer 1960. Initially, W.O. drove it himself. He was able to do a good number of small jobs such as single drains out of ponds, including a semi-industrial job on a housing development in Darlington. The only bucket that came with it was 15 inches wide, with one set of side cutters taking it up to 18 inches and another set up to 21 inches.

One of the first problems he came up with, particularly on farm work, was the difficulty in getting the clay out of the bucket. Much of the clay he was digging through was the black silt-like variety that sticks to everything. It became apparent that all the vigorous shaking of the dipper arm was probably doing more harm to the machine than the actual digging was. An 18-inch trench was also going to be too wide for field drainage, particularly when permeable fill was to be used. Whitlock's sold a 10-inch bucket with an ejector flap inside it to clean this silt clay out. We bought one but unfortunately the bucket was fixed in place by two rigid stays at the back and the crowd ram was used to operate the ejector. All this meant that there was no means of levelling the bucket or of crowding it when full. You were therefore digging with the bucket for most of the time not at the correct angle, with no means to crowd it up when full.

We had been able to secure our first grant-aided field drainage scheme for the autumn of that year. It was a scheme of almost 100 chains, which would only have been two days' work for a modern trencher but for a hydraulic back actor with an inexperienced crew would represent several weeks' work. Harvest was almost finished when the weather broke, so they took the digger to this field and made a start on the main drain that ran along the bottom of it. Remember what I said about a steep learning curve? Well, at that point in time no drain tiles had been delivered to the site and no methods of checking the grading was available. They dug out and scooped the bottom of

approximately 5 to 6 chains of drain that day. The following day, the weather took up again so it was back to finishing combining and baling.

The workforce at that time consisted of W.O. and his brothers, Eddie and Walter Robson. I was still at school. It was therefore difficult to keep the drainage going when there was so much other general contracting to do. Once harvesting was completed there would be so much autumn ploughing and rotavating and there was still quite a bit of threshing, which was relatively quiet during the autumn but continuous from Christmas to March.

Consequently it was three weeks before they were able to resume draining. The first thing they found was that the trench sides had collapsed and fallen in and water had become trapped in what remained of the trench. It was a complete mess. The decision was taken to abandon the first trench and dig a new one alongside. Drain pipes were now on site and a start was made in laying them in this new trench. The field was quite undulating and there was no positive means of grading. By the second day it was obvious that in places these pipes had water halfway up them. So the pipes had to be lifted out and the trench bottom graded by drainage scoop, using the water that had collected in the trench as a guide to the correct levels.

The farmer was most understanding; he did not need the field until spring, so we were able to carry on at our own pace between threshing and ploughing. By the week before Christmas we only had two short drains left to do. In those days we worked Saturday mornings as a matter of course, so on this particular Saturday I drove the digger. At around eleven o'clock the machine stopped digging. The tractor was still running but there was no hydraulic motion. As it was close to dinner time we left it and went home.

On the others' return to the site on the Monday morning they found that the four bolts that secured the digger to the tractor's right-hand axle had sheared off, allowing the digging unit to swing to one side. This had trapped the main hydraulic feed pipe from the front-mounted pump, preventing oil reaching the digging unit. They pulled the digger back with the winch and managed to free the pipe. The digger unit was temporally secured in place by a rope and the machine was then driven back to the yard and parked in a shed.

We had already being having discussions amongst ourselves to the effect that we probably had the wrong machine for the job.

The War Ag were draining in the area with rotary trenchers and doing a job in a week that would have taken us more than a month. There didn't seem to be very much ditch cleaning coming our way, but plenty of tile drainage work. During this autumn we had secured another job from a local farmer and another two quite large schemes from land agents Smith Gore working on behalf of the Church Commissioners. With these three jobs having to be done by March (and the possibility of other jobs to come) and the digger broken down, we needed to act promptly. At this point in time the rotary trench digger market was dominated by the Howard machine, which was fitted

The Mark 111 Whitlock Dinkum Digger.

with Rotaped tracks in place of the rear tractor wheels and steel front wheels with a deep rib on them. We did not have any form of low loading trailer so moving any kind of tracked machine was going to be a problem. In the previous year, Howard's had been advertising their machines with Roadless four-wheel drive conversions in place of the Rotapeds. Although more costly, this would obviously solve the transport problem. As time went on we were coming more and more round to the idea of a Howard trencher.

There were two agents for Howard trenchers that we knew of. We contacted both to ask if they would be prepared to take the Dinkum Digger in part exchange for a new trencher. Both were interested but wanted to see our machine before talking money, and our machine was somewhat disabled. I was on Christmas holidays when this was going on, and we agreed that, to make it suitable for sale, we would have to look at this digger and try to drill the broken studs out from underneath the axle.

On this particular day, W.O. was away threshing and he said to me the night before, "Have a look at that digger and see what is going to be needed to get it going again." The next morning, the first thing I did was jack the machine up and take the back wheel off. With that removed I could get a good view of the problem. There was a footplate for the driver's foot in the digging position that had one stud into the top of the axle housing, and underneath it were the four sheared-off bolts. There was a block of wood nearby, which I sat on to study the problem. One thing I was certain of was that I did not relish the idea of lying on my back and trying to drill four studs out from under the axle. I was sure that in order to get them out, the half-shaft housing would need to be removed from the tractor, turned

over and drilled down over in the workshop. As I sat there I was looking at the grease nipple, which all Fordson Majors had behind the outer bearing. What I noticed was that there was another grease nipple on the front of the axle in addition to the usual one behind. So, I thought, why would they do that? Nobody would ever grease it; very few people would know it was there … and who cared, anyway? I came to the conclusion that it was done so that all these half-shaft castings would be the same, so that in the factory they wouldn't have right and left housings, but any housing could go on either side and it wouldn't matter which way up they were used. With that I was onto something. Why couldn't I turn that half-shaft housing upside down so that I wouldn't need to remove those studs? The only problem I could see was that the footplate could not be bolted down.

So I then got started. It was a relatively simple matter to take the row of studs out that secured this casting to the main transmission housing, rotating it through 180 degrees and re-bolting it. I had a bit more difficulty aligning the holes in the digging frame to these holes now under the axle, to which I then fitted four new ¾-inch bolts. The footplate was secured at the back but was then just laid on top of the axle. It was then simply a matter of refitting the wheel, and the job was complete.

The two sales representatives visited in the next few days and eventually a deal was done. We had been dealing with the Lancashire firm of Preston Farmers since our Marshall tractor days, and it was they who secured the order for the new trencher. That machine with the Roadless four-wheel drive conversion was delivered on the 18th January 1961, and was taxed for the road with registration number YAJ 41.

The Howard trencher on pneumatic tyres.

Rotary Trenchers

Steam-powered rotary trench diggers can be traced back as far as the late nineteenth century in North America. The Cleveland Pacific Company of Cleveland, Ohio, and Buckeye of Windsor, Ontario were the first to produce such machines. By 1917, the Buckeye had progressed to an oil engine and the Cleveland presumably about the same time. They were both of the open wheel type, developed initially for the installation of water and sewage systems. The open wheel is supported by rollers referred to as truck rollers. The Buckeye had four sets arranged in a square formation whilst the Cleveland had three in a triangular formation. These early machines were available with various cutting widths, which in some cases could be up to 2 feet wide

and needing great power. The Buckeye was largely a fabricated structure using various engines that were available at that time. Most of these machines were mounted on crawler tracks, but the Buckeye was available in the 1930s and 40s on pneumatic tyres, being built onto a truck chassis and cab. This was a six-wheel configuration with the two rear axles both powered, and on some machines the facility was there to apply power to the front axle as well. Some Buckeye machines were imported to the UK under the Lend-Lease scheme of the Second World War. The Cleveland was of similar construction but it used an International tractor skid unit as its power source. Both firms are still in business, offering a wide variety of sizes of machine.

A Buckeye trencher.

Eric Clayton's Cleveland trencher, being driven by Ian Whitfield.

In the inter-war years there was less labour available for digging drains by hand on schemes involving whole fields. Rope excavators were used to some extent with their dragline or Teredo equipment, but there was clearly a need for a more compact form of trench-digging device. Henderson's of Glasgow developed a form of rotary trench digger in the late 1930s. Mounted on a Standard Fordson tractor, this machine could make quite an acceptable drainage trench.

The Henderson trench digger on a Standard Fordson.

Drive was taken from the tractor's PTO point, along the right-hand side of the tractor, to a gearbox with a cross-shaft with crank arms on either end. The digging was done by a star wheel with six digging paddles arranged around it. From the cranks at the front of the machine, connecting rods transmitted power to a ratcheting device that rotated the star wheel. Each rotation of the crank moved the star wheel on by one paddle. Behind the driver's seat, and driven from the trencher's gearbox, was a winch drum. The rope from this winch went down the back of

the tractor around a fairlead, then along under the tractor and out to some form of anchor point a way ahead. The machine was raised and lowered by a small hand-operated, winch which could also be used for grading the trench bottom. However, with a maximum digging depth of 2 feet 6 inches, it would need to be at full depth for most of the time.

Henderson's continued with this and developments of it into the 1960s. They were clearly targeting the farmer, as opposed to drainage contractors, with their machines, which were always just tractor attachments.

A closed wheel trench digger was developed by Mr John Howard in the late 1930s, and was on sale from 1942 onwards. Mr Howard was an Australian who developed power-driven rotary cultivators. The British manufacturing business was known as Rotary Hoes Ltd.

The Howard trencher on a Standard Fordson equipped with Rotaped tracks.

Their machine was built onto a Standard Fordson tractor. The drive to this trencher was taken from the right-hand side of the tractor, where a belt pulley would normally be fitted. It was taken by an enclosed shaft back to a bevel box and cross-shaft that formed the front of the trench-digging unit. This shaft extended to left of centre of the tractor to where a sprocket in an enclosed chain case took the drive back to the centre of the digging wheel, where some spur reduction gears drove the rotor. This chain case used heavy plate and formed the only support for the digging wheel. A Samson post was fabricated, rising up from the left-hand tractor axle with a hand-operated winch on top that formed the raising and lowering mechanism for the digging wheel. There were 12 L-shaped blades fitted to this wheel, which could dig to depths of 36 inches. Soil was brought up in the blades to the top of the rotor, where angled scrapers cleaned them. The soil then dropped onto a mouldboard, which pushed this soil away from the trench side leaving a neat row close to the trench. Crumb left by the blades was collected by an adjustable web-type scraper, which kept the trench clean and free from crumb.

The tractor was fitted with a 24-1 reduction gearbox to give the required speed for trench digging. The tractor's back wheels were replaced by Rotaped tracks, manufactured by Howard's themselves. A large sprocket was fitted to the tractor half-shaft and six track pads were arranged around it. Roller chains within the Rotaped needed to be kept well tensioned to keep the sprocket engaged with the inside of the track pads. The tractor's front wheels were replaced with heavy cast wheels with a deep rib running round them.

These machines became widespread during the Second World War, when there was pressure to increase food production by improving marginal land. The War Ag operated a great number of these machines on Standard Fordsons, which as they were replaced into the 1950s were sold off, and some farmers bought them themselves.

The Howard trench digger was adapted to fit the E27N Major after the war. The drive from the belt pulley point was discontinued and a bolt-on gearbox was made to fit around the PTO shaft, with bevel gears taking the drive to the chain case. Sales of that particular model were low and very few are known to still be in existence. The diameter of the rotor was increased, giving a working depth of 42 inches. A hydraulic ram was fitted between the top of the Samson post and the chain case, although the winch was retained for transport and any emergencies. Remote controls were fitted for the driver to walk by the left-hand side of the digging wheel and adjust the depth and steering from that position.

TRENCH SCRAPER SIDE-PLATE ADJUSTING HANDLE

TRENCH SCRAPER ADJUSTING HANDLE

MOULD BOARD WINCH CONTROL HANDLE INCORPORATING AUTOMATIC HYDRAULIC CONTROLLED DEPTH CONTROL

ROTOR HYDRAULIC CONTROL LEVER

ROTOR HOISTING WINCH HANDLE

CLUTCH

STEERING

REDUCTION GEAR LEVER

ROTOR ENGAGING LEVER

The Howard trench digger when fitted to the E1A Fordson Major.

Eric Clayton's two Howard trenchers. Nearest to the camera is a Super trencher on a Power Major with Perkins engine. The other one is a standard trencher on a Fordson Major with a Fordson engine. To the right-hand side of the machines is a Cowley level on its tripod.

A contented looking drainage gang.

Sighting poles with adjustable crossbars were provided with the machine. The poles were set up in a straight line 3 feet to the left of where the drain was to be and the crossbars were set in line at a suitable gradient. A bracket was mounted on the front of the tractor with a vertical rod that was kept in line with the sight poles. On the trencher unit a sight bar was located near to the remote driving position. The driver now could grade accurately and steer as he progressed along the trench. The other controls he had included an adjusting handle to vary the height of the mouldboard as the trench depth varied, and a hand clutch. For everything else – gear change, throttle, PTO engagement – he had to walk to the tractor driving position.

There were practically no modifications needed to the trencher to fit it to the new Major in 1952. Howard's at this time began to offer a pipe-laying attachment. This consisted of two steel plates projecting rearward from the trench scraper, and a tile shoot, which started high up behind the trench scraper, went down into

The reduction gearbox fitted in the Fordson Major's transmission.

the box and curved into the horizontal position on the trench floor. It would hold approximately eight 12-inch long drain pipes, which was sufficient weight to keep the pipes firmly butted up in the trench.

Two years later came the Super trench digger, which became known as the Mark III. This had an even bigger digging wheel and could dig to 48 inches deep. This extra depth created more soil on the mouldboard so a soil spinner was fitted to scatter the spoil over a larger area. A drive shaft was taken from the trencher's gearbox, taking the drive to a bevel box at the right-hand side of the machine. Then a drive shaft with two universal joints took the drive back to a second bevel box with the four-arm spinner mounted underneath it. The reduction gearbox was further reduced with a 32-1 reduction now being deployed. Howard's felt that with the increased digging depth the Fordson engine of 40 horsepower would be inadequate, so they fitted the Perkins L4, which was rated at 56 horsepower.

By 1959, The Fordson had become the Power Major, with 51 horsepower, and the Perkins L4 had become the Four 270D, which was now up to 65 horsepower. The general rule was that the trench digger used the Fordson engine and the Super trench digger had the Perkins fitted but, like all rules, there were exceptions, and some standard trenchers came out with the Perkins engine. The other change was that Roadless four-wheel drive conversion was offered as an alternative to the Rotapeds.

The major problem with these trenchers was that when lifting, the machine pivoted around the front shaft behind the tractor. As the depth was decreased the trench scraper lifted off the trench bottom, allowing crumb to pass underneath it. The tile shoot was held within some moveable plates so that it could rise and fall as the trench depth varied, but with variable amounts of crumb escaping under the scraper it meant that you couldn't rely on the tiles being accurately graded. As we moved into the 1960s, competitor machines were coming onto the market with parallel lifting arrangements that were superior to that of the Howard.

By 1961, they had developed the Howard Super 66. This was a much bigger machine that could dig down to 66 inches. It was a full-track machine with a Fordson six-cylinder engine. The tractor skid unit was sourced from County's, with their clutch and brake steering system as used on the County crawlers. Howard's own reduction gearbox was used in the transmission line, giving the required speed for trenching.

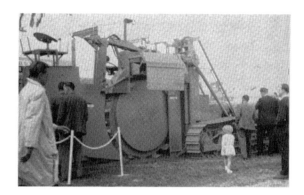

The Howard Super 66 on its introduction in 1961.

The Howard Super 66 as it looks today.

The Mark IV trencher on Rotapeds.

This machine would have been an extremely expensive one to make and could not have been competitively priced. I have no information as to how successful it was in operation and cannot tell if it ever got beyond the prototype stage. I know of the existence of one machine. Were there any more?

In 1965 they marketed the Mark IV trench digger. This was built around the Ford 5000 tractor and was offered on Rotapeds or four-wheel drive pneumatics, which in this case were equal-sized wheels from the County 654 tractor. The difference to the Mark III was that a parallel lifting arrangement similar to the Super 66 was used. The drive to the trench digger was taken from the top of the tractor's gearbox from a place where the tractor's hydraulic lift would normally have sat. Bevel boxes and shafts brought the drive to the right-hand side of the tractor, where

The tracks were of the sprocket and chain type with bolt-on cleated grousers, and supplied to Howard's by the Marshall Fowler company. The trench digger had a vertical lifting system on some vertical channel section beams. These were held rigidly so as to allow the digging wheel to penetrate the ground; if no inset had been dug, the rear crumber and tile layer could be lifted hydraulically. The drive to the digging wheel was taken from the belt pulley power point on the right-hand side of the Fordson tractor via a long telescopic shaft to a bevel gearbox situated above the digging wheel. From this point a cross-shaft took the drive to a chain case on the left of the machine, which went to the centre of the wheel, as had been the case with the older Howards. There was a seat in the normal tractor driving position, and a further one on the left-hand side of the digging wheel. This remote driving position had all the controls needed, including two gear levers, clutch, steering controls, throttle and hydraulics.

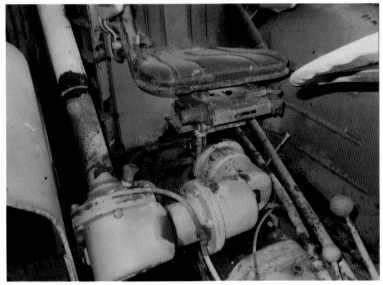

The drive from tractor gearbox to digging wheel followed a tortuous route.

a telescopic drive shaft took power up to the digging wheel, very much as on the Super 66. This had the normal tractor seating position. Then a remote driving position, as on the earlier machines, was a walking one on the right-hand side of the digging wheel. As on the Super 66, there were many more controls routed back to that remote position: two gear levers, on the 5000 two clutches, steering, hydraulics and throttle.

A publicity photograph of the Mark IV machine mounted on a County 654 tractor.

Howard Trench Digger Mark IV.

The Howard Mark V.

This had been a more successful machine than the Super 66. Nevertheless, production of this particular model ceased by the end of the decade. In 1970 it was replaced by the Mark V. This was a complete departure from anything Howard's had done hitherto. It was a full-track machine with a digging chain in place of the solid wheel. It still used the Ford skid unit as its power source, but this time with the six-cylinder engine giving 100 horsepower. On the tractor's half-shafts' ends were large sprockets, which ran in the top of the track and acted as a top roller. There was an idler at each end of the track, with five intermediate bottom rollers. The drive to the digging chain was taken from the front of the engine crankshaft, and transferred by a long shaft running along the left-hand side of the engine to a

bevel gearbox on the top shaft of the digging chain. The remote driving position was now a seated one located on the right-hand side of the machine.

In 1961, Allen's of Oxford, who had sold the ATOS digger in the 1950s and then went on to concentrate on crane production, introduced their open wheel trencher. This was very much based on the American Cleveland trencher but they used the Fordson Super Major as the power source. The digging wheel was supported in its frame by truck rollers, one pair at the rear of the frame, another at the bottom of the wheel on triangular supports. Then, at the front, there were combined rollers and driving sprockets. There were two vertical frame members within

An Allen's publicity photographs of the Mark I.

the tracks that the trencher slid up and down on. Two hydraulic rams were positioned over what would have been the tractor driving position. Wire ropes passed over pulleys at the top of the vertical frame, which were then attached to the trencher frame. These ropes divided into two, with one set going to the front of the trencher frame and the other to the back.

Two ring plates with toothed segments formed the digging wheel, with curved buckets holding the two together. It was claimed that it could make a trench 9, 12 or 15 inches wide and down to 4 feet 6 inches in depth. It was this configuration that gave it the name Allen 9/15 Landraner. At the top of the wheel there was a tongue projecting into the buckets to clean all the spoil out of them and drop it onto a cross-conveyor. This rubber-belted conveyor was chain-driven from a sprocket on a small gearbox located under the conveyor, which took its drive from the main sprocket shaft of the digging unit. This gearbox had a lever on the side of it that altered the direction of rotation of the conveyor. It could also be wound through the machine from side to side to place the spoil as near or distant as was required. The drive to the digging wheel was taken from the PTO shaft on the tractor via a chain running up to a large gearbox mounted on top of the tractor's transmission housing. From this box shafts with chain sprockets on them protruded from either side. Within this gearbox was a reversing mechanism so that the digging wheel could be reversed if needed. The two chains took the drive back to two sprockets on the shaft through the digging wheel. As the trencher moved up and down the vertical frame these chains needed to vary in length. Two spring-loaded idler sprockets ran in the slack chain to the top of the run.

The machine was on full tracks but they were what could be described as poor quality tracks. Metal tracks can be divided into two types: all-steel ones, fitted to crawler tractors where a sprocket at the rear drives a chain around a front idler, which then has cleated grouser plates bolted to it; and the cast pad and tumbler type, which has pads with teeth cast into them for the tumbler sprockets to drive into. These pads are then fastened together with pins to make a continuous track. The cast pad and tumbler type of track was usually fitted to cranes and large excavators, which did not travel very far in the course of a day. On the Allen, a sprocket was fitted to the tractor half-shafts and a roller chain took the drive down to the track sprockets, which were at the front of the track and completely the wrong way round. The tracks were 16 inches wide by 6 feet 6 inches long, and it steered with the tractor's disc brakes.

A two-position reduction box was fitted behind the tractor's own gearbox, giving two ranges of working gears. Over the right-hand track was a chequer plate walkway, with a seat near to the front, facing the tractor. The driver had two hydraulic controls in front of him, a hand clutch and a hand-steering lever. From that point he could reach the gear levers and throttle handle, albeit with some difficulty. He also had the handle for engaging or reversing the digging wheel.

On the front of the tractor was a vertical sighting rod to keep the machine in line with the sight poles up the field. There was also a grading crossbar suspended over the centre of the digging wheel. This sight-level bar was higher off the ground than the human eye. Therefore, two crossbars were needed on the Allen sight poles with a fixed distance between, usually 2 feet 6 inches.

The trench scraper was fitted rigidly to the machine and the tile layer was firmly bolted to it. The practice when trenching was to allow the back ropes to hang slack and do all the grading with the front ropes The tile layer was all in one piece and the tile shoot was fixed to the bottom of it. A seat was provided for the tile-laying man, as well as a tray beside him where a small number of pipes could be carried. The machine was finished in orange.

It was little over a year before the machine was modified into Mark II. The only difference was that the driver now had a remote driving position for driving while trenching. A small driver's platform was created on the right-hand side of the machine just in front of the cross-conveyor. Situated there was a remote clutch lever, hydraulic controls, a cable-operated throttle control and remote controlled steering with a steering wheel. The hydraulic and steering were connected to the remote driving position by telescopic hexagonal rods with small universal joints. Like the Mark I, the Mark II model was finished in orange livery.

Les Clark on a Mark III Allen, overlooking the sea near Saltburn.

The Mark III, which followed in 1964, was the same machine with a slight increase in track size – 18 inches wide and 7 feet 6 inches long – and eight bottom rollers in place of the six on previous models. With the Mark III the colour was changed from orange to yellow.

The Mark IV became available for 1966, and this represented the biggest shake-up that the Allen trencher had had so far. The first change, which was forced upon them, was that the Fordson Super Major was replaced by the Ford 5000 as the power source. This increased the power from 53 horsepower to 65. It now had the benefit of oil immersed brakes, which gave more positive steering than the old dry discs had done. The biggest change, however, was to the tracks. The new ones were the type with chain and bolt-on grousers, in this case with three ribs, and the driving sprockets were now at the back. Width and length were increased and, as with the Mark III, eight bottom rollers were deployed.

Allen's publicity photograph of the Mark IV.

Our first Allen Mark IV.

With the change to the Ford 5000 the trencher now benefitted from independent PTO, which meant that the digging wheel could be started with the tracks stationary. Allen's gearbox mounted on the tractor transmission housing, taking the drive from the power take-off shaft to the digging wheel, now had a differential fitted between the two side sprockets. With the earlier machines it was difficult to keep both side chains under equal tension, with the consequence that one chain would be doing all the work. The cross-conveyor was shortened, but still adequate for field drainage work, and it was now driven by a hydraulic motor. The two bottom truck rollers in the digging wheel became four. A pivoted rocking beam was fitted to the triangular frame, with a pair of rollers at each end. On the earlier machines some of the remote driving controls used telescopic hexagonal rods, which were now replaced by cables. There were various other changes, including that the main lifting rams now pushed to lift. The colour remained as the Mark III, yellow.

Les Clark on his Mark IV. This machine was fitted with the six-cylinder engine.

This machine remained virtually unchanged from this point onwards. In 1968, it received the Ford Force 5000 power unit, which increased the power to 75 horsepower. It was now known as the Mark IVA, but very little was changed to the wheeled trencher. As the 1960s gave way to the 1970s, the chain trenchers were gaining in popularity. To remain competitive, Allen's announced their 'chaindrain' machine. This simply replaced the digging wheel with a chain type trencher. The same lifting system was used and the same drive chains.

The chain trencher developed by Caley's of Burton Pidsea.

Caley's of Burton Pidsea, near Hull, were agents for Allen trenchers at this time and they developed their own version of the Allen chaindrain. It used a hydraulic motor for the main drive in place of the side chains. They also developed their own lifting system and boom type lift for the tile layer, dispensing with the wire ropes.

In continental Europe there were several trencher manufacturers producing machines in the post-war years. The most prolific country producing trenchers was the Netherlands. By 1959, they had makes such as Barth, Van Den Ende, and Steenbergen Hollanddrain. As in the UK, early Dutch machines used farm tractors for their power source. The Van Den Ende was mounted on an International Farmall tractor, with the rear wheels removed and replaced by sprockets with chains driving the tracks.

The Van Den Ende machine, with the Farmall as its power source.

The Barth machine, with the Fordson Major in the reverse position.

The Farmall's front axle was retained and used as steering for the trencher. The Barth used the Fordson Major as its power source, but with the tractor mounted the opposite way round to the usual way. It had its PTO shaft at the front and its radiator at the back, facing the digging mechanism. The track sprockets were positioned directly onto the tractor half-shafts, and the drive to the trench digger was taken from the tractor's power take-off by a chain, then a shaft that took the drive back to the digging chain.

Some sales literature for Barth machines of the early 1960s showed closed wheel, open wheel and chain trenchers, but it has to be said that they were most successful with their chain machine. The fertiliser manufacturers Fisons ran a contracting service in the sixties. It was located around East Anglia and the Fens and known as Fisons Farm Work Ltd. They had imported several of the Barth closed wheel type trenchers, which were suitable for the stone-free fenland soils.

Barth (Holland) opened a manufacturing facility at Mablethorpe in Lincolnshire in 1962, which was known as Barth (Great Britain). As the sixties progressed, the Dutch machines increased in size and output, and required much more power than tractor engines or transmissions were capable of. They were then using large six-cylinder lorry engines and transmissions specially developed for their needs. Of course, there were now no tractor bonnets, only some crude fabricated arrangements. The Barth machines imported from Holland were large full-track machines, for the most part with chain type trenchers. The chain trenchers were simply a large chain on a carrier arm driven by the top sprocket, and an idler at the bottom end. The chain was fitted with cutting blades, which did the work of bringing the spoil up the front, where an auger, with flights running both ways, scattered the spoil to each side. In the centre of this auger was a sprocket, which ran in the chain and was allowed to rise and fall with ground level. Barth began manufacturing the K140 at Mablethorpe in the late 1960s. This was smaller than the Dutch

machines and used a Ford 5000 as its power source. It was a full-tracked machine with the track-driving sprockets being direct on the tractors half-shafts, and the track running over them in a triangular formation.

Some sales literature for Barth machines of the early 1960s showed closed wheel, open wheel and chain trenchers, but it has to be said that they were most successful with their chain machine. The fertiliser manufacturers Fisons ran a contracting service in the sixties. It was located around East Anglia and the Fens and known as Fisons Farm Work Ltd. They had imported several of the Barth closed wheel type trenchers, which were suitable for the stone-free fenland soils.

Barth (Holland) opened a manufacturing facility at Mablethorpe in Lincolnshire in 1962, which was known as Barth (Great Britain). As the sixties progressed, the Dutch machines increased in size and output, and required much more power than tractor engines or transmissions were capable of. They were then using large six-cylinder lorry engines and transmissions specially developed for their needs. Of course, there were now no tractor bonnets, only some crude fabricated arrangements. The Barth machines imported from Holland were large full-track machines, for the most part with chain type trenchers. The chain trenchers were simply a large chain on a carrier arm driven by the top sprocket, and an idler at the bottom end. The chain was fitted with cutting blades, which did the work of bringing the spoil up the front, where an auger, with flights running both ways, scattered the spoil to each side. In the centre of this auger was a sprocket, which ran in the chain and was allowed to rise and fall with ground level. Barth began manufacturing the K140 at Mablethorpe in the late 1960s. This was smaller than the Dutch machines and used a Ford 5000 as its power source. It was a full-tracked machine with the track-driving sprockets being direct on the tractors half-shafts, and the track running over them in a triangular formation.

The Barth K140 machine.

The Muir Hill trencher.

Some other Dutch machines were imported in the 1960s and 1970s. They were all large full-track machines with chain trench digging arrangements, and engines in excess of 100 horsepower. One had two engines, with one driving the digging chain and one the tracks.

Another make of trencher to come onto the British market in the late 1960s was sold as a Muir Hill. Muir Hill had been making a range of loading shovels and other industrial type machinery in the post-war years, and in the mid-1960s developed a range of agricultural tractors. These tractors were based around the Ford 5000 tractor, but most had six-cylinder engines and equal sized four-wheel drive. Unlike Roadless and County, they made their own bonnet and nose cone, and finished them off in industrial yellow. The trencher was made by Radahl of Norway. It was a closed wheel type, driven by a hydraulic motor. It had a 24-1 reduction gearbox, which they bought from Howard's. There was a vertical pillar behind the tractor, which the digging mechanism slid up and down. This pillar could be tilted forwards to allow the wheel to dig its own starting trench when no inset had been previously dug. It did not have a remote driving position for trenching, but the driver sat in the normal tractor seat, with a sight bar coming over his head from behind and a suspended crossbar in front of him. It cut an 8-inch trench as standard, with an optional 10-inch line available, and had a maximum working depth of 5 feet.

There were other makes of trencher, from both British and overseas manufacturers, which were aimed mainly at the industrial sector and had very little impact on the agricultural scene. Among them were Winget-Parson, and Bruff.

The Mark III Allen trencher waiting to start another drain at Brotton on the North Sea coast.

Land Drainage: A Brief History

A field at Grange Farm, Girsby, North Yorkshire, drained in the 1860s on a herringbone pattern with laterals in excess of 3 feet in depth and clearly still working.

In the early 1850s, artificial manures or, as we would now say, fertilisers, became available and farmers were prepared to use them on a considerable scale. However, they knew that applying fertilisers to waterlogged ground would not give a satisfactory return, so they pressed their landlords into draining the land. The terms of the public loans for land improvement are not known but they were subject to annual repayments. In addition to the government loans, others became available from private companies as well, running from the late 1840s until 1890. The landowners took full advantage of this funding to help their tenants, who otherwise were in danger of bankruptcy.

Records were not kept as to how many acres were drained in this period but it was a considerable number. Similarly, exact details of the terms of the loans were not made available but, again, they must have been benign as during the twentieth century these drains were referred to as 'government drains'. At this time some early levelling devices, such as theodolites, were available, and so we saw fairly comprehensive well-thought-out drainage schemes. These drains did not always run up and down the major slope; some were laid at an angle across the slope. It was during this period that we saw for the first time what was to become known as the 'herringbone' system, where a main drain was laid up the centre of the field, with laterals extending out from both sides and at an angle up the slope. These drains were laid to a very high standard at depths of between 3 and 4 feet, and many of them are still performing well to this day.

From 1850 onwards, a certain amount of prosperity was enjoyed by farmers. The combination of draining the land and the use of artificial fertilisers helped to boost output. I still see evidence of this as I look around the traditional farm buildings, many of which were built during the 1880s and 1890s. But as the funding for drainage work ceased in the 1890s, major drainage projects were no longer carried out and British agriculture became less prosperous. Consequently, from then until 1939, farming experienced difficult times. It is apparent when looking,

for example, at farm buildings that very little in the way of construction was done during that period.

Southern Ireland had for centuries been a source of hand labourers. Indeed, they were known as 'Irish navvies' and they were originally employed on the digging of canals, and then for the construction of the railways. In the 1840s, the Irish potato crop failed for three consecutive years, causing great hardship and starvation for the rural communities. Many families emigrated to America. Ireland was at that time part of the United Kingdom, so many others came to the British mainland and were employed as labourers for the digging of land drainage ditches and trenches.

An example of some of the hand tools used in digging drainage trenches. On the left is a scoop for levelling the trench bottom, a short spit useful in the trench for removing stones etc. and a normal digging spade and a trench digging spit.

From the time of the withdrawal of government funding in 1890 to 1939, very few comprehensive drainage schemes were laid down. Farmers would simply lay one or two drains into a wet place, and the surrounding areas would be left undrained. We know that this was not a satisfactory solution; the best way to dry up a wet area is to lay drains around it to intercept the water before it reaches the wet area.

The first clay tiles to be manufactured were open-bottom or horseshoe type. The reason for the open bottom was that brickworks did not have the technology to make round pipes. They took a piece of clay as for a roof tile and moulded it round a circular wooden former before it went into the kiln. It was for this reason that drain 'pipes' were more often referred to as tiles or drain tiles. They could either be laid directly onto clay, or onto slate or flat stones if the ground was considered too soft. The next step was to close the bottom of the pipe. Some firms were reluctant to seal the two sides to make an enclosed pipe, arguing that an open seam was needed to allow water to enter the drain. It may, however, have been that they did not know how to close the seam. Completely closed tiles appeared first in the mid-nineteenth century, when brickworks had mastered the art of making round pipes. It was done by extrusion: wet clay was forced through a die the shape of a drain tile. This process took considerable power and it was only with the coming of the steam engine that brickworks were able to achieve this. The pipes were then cut into lengths before going to the kiln to be fired, so creating the hard red tile that we are all familiar with. Early round tiles still retained their flat bottom; it was to be some years before drain tiles became completely round. The length of 1 foot was not standardised until the early years of the twentieth century.

At Henry Oakland – a firm of drain tile makers at Escrick, near York – is where I saw this extrusion process going on. The clay was being squeezed through the formers, making three pipes at one time – two on the bottom and one above. Either side

A selection of drain tiles. To the right-hand side are some early flat-bottom pipes, the others are more modern round tiles of various diameters. The one on the extreme left-hand side has ribs on the outside, indicating that it was made by the London Brick Company.

The open-bottom horseshoe drain tile.

Removing drain pipes from the kiln at the Alne Brick Company works near Easingwold, in Yorkshire. The method used was by wheelbarrows, in this case two. They were then wheeled out into the yard and stacked to await collection by a lorry.

From 1890 to 1939, there was very little machinery available for digging drains, so many of them were laid at too shallow a depth. The 1920s and 1930s were difficult years for farming and attention to drainage needs was not uppermost in the farmers' minds, so there was a lot of neglect. The result was that by 1939, home produced food had fallen to something in the order of 30 per cent of need.

of these wet pipes, chains were running slowly, with taut wires between them. A wire would descend through the clay, creating a perfect clean cut, and then the next wire would appear exactly 12 inches further along the pipe. Original diameters were from as little as 1 inch up to 6 inches, with 2 and 3 inches being the most common. The 1-inch pipes were soon dropped; 2-inch ones were made into the twentieth century before also being dropped. From that time onwards, clay pipes were available in 3-, 4- and 6-inch diameters, all 1 foot long. Also available were 9-inch diameter pipes, but we normally used pipes made of other materials when laying a 9-inch drain.

The hand tools required for drainage work have hardly changed for centuries. When draining by hand labour, the first thing used was a spade. This was used to take the first layer of soil from the trench. The trench at this stage needed to have some width – probably 12 to 15 inches – to enable a man to stand in and work. If it was to be a deep drain, there could be two or three spade depths to be taken out, in which case there needed to be room for a man's hips to move in the trench. The next thing needed was a draining spit, similar to a spade but with a longer and narrower curved blade.

In the yard at Alne Brick Company in the 1960s, a man is wheeling a barrow load of pipes, in this case, junction pipes, past a stack of 3-inch pipes awaiting collection.

These blades were approximately 15 inches long and would be driven down to the full depth by a man's weight on the foot rest. The next thing needed was a drainage scoop, a curved blade with handle attached at approximately a 30 degree angle. Some scoops had the handle at one end and were suitable only for pulling towards the operator, others had the handle attached about one third of the way along it and could be pulled or pushed. The ones we preferred had a horseshoe arrangement in the centre of the scoop, which again could be pulled or pushed. The curve on the blade was the same as

Another selection of drainage tools, including two different types of drainage scoop and a trench digging spit.

the curve of a drain pipe, of 3, 4, or 6 inches. Scoops could also have different length shafts and different angles of attachment, allowing the man to work either in the trench or alongside it. When scooping behind a rotary trencher we used long-shafted scoops to enable the operator to stand on the field surface, but behind a digger making a wider trench, a shorter-shafted scoop with the man working in the trench was the preferred option. The last hand tool was the tile hook. This was a shaft similar to a fork shaft, with a steel rod fastened to one end at right angles. A man could lift a drain tile on this hook and lower it into the trench, and then rotate the pipe to get it to lie better and make a closer joint with the previous one.

The Hilger and Watts pocket level.

Devices to check levels became essential pieces of drainage equipment. First of these was a sight gauge, or pocket level, simply a square tube about 1 inch square by 5 inches long, with a small aperture in one end and a wire across the other end. It also incorporated a spirit level.

An image of the spirit level appeared within the tube, so you held it level and looked through the aperture to the wire and beyond. If, for instance, from normal eye level of 5 feet looking across a field, the wires line ran into the ground before the far hedge, that meant there was more than 5 feet of fall across the field. If, on the other hand, you were looking at the tree tops, then there was fall away from you. This was a very crude level and only intended to be a rough guide, but it was quite useful when planning a drainage scheme. A Cowley level was designed for use by builders, but was a very useful piece of equipment for us, albeit with limitations on range. It was essentially a box on a tripod with a series of mirrors suspended inside it. By looking in a lens on the top of it your vision was reflected through a hole in the front of it, giving a split view: a normal view and an inverted one. It then needed a second man with a staff, with feet and inches marked up it, and a crossbar, which this operator moved up or down as directed by the man at the instrument. That man's job was to line the two images

of the crossbar up into a straight line, at which point the man with the staff would read the measurement off the staff. That measurement meant nothing until another reading was taken some distance away and the two readings compared. The staff had an extension with it, allowing it to be used on pipes in the drain. A more sophisticated device was the dumpy level, manufactured by Hilger and Watts. This had a more substantial tripod, with the instrument at eye level. There was a circular spirit level for fitting the instrument to the tripod before securing.

The dumpy level manufactured by Hilger and Watts.

The instrument was telescopic and the staff that accompanied it had numbers printed on it. As one looked through the instrument there was a further spirit level, which was much more accurate. This telescopic device had the effect of inverting the image. The numbers on the staff were also upside down, but it could nevertheless be read some considerable distance away. It was now up to the man reading the staff to write down the readings, with their locations, for future reference. These were considered to be the best type and were recognised and accepted by Ministry officials.

The dumpy level on its tripod.

The dumpy level staff, with imperial measurements. These are in feet, and then tenths of feet; the Roman V is used in place of 5 so as not to be confused with a 3 when viewed from a distance.

Grant-Aided Schemes

The Ministry of Agriculture's involvement was part of the government's attempt to increase home produced food during the war. Farmers had just survived the depression years of the 1930s and weren't in any mood to start spending large sums of money on drainage and scrub clearance. There clearly had to be some incentive to encourage them, and this came in the form of government grants. The government would pay a 50 per cent grant towards the cost of drainage and ditching work on condition that a government-approved scheme was adhered to. There weren't many contractors with the heavy machinery needed to carry out this work. The government's contracting arm, the War Ag, were equipped with all the heavy plant needed to do drainage, ditching and scrub clearance.

All English counties had Ministry of Agriculture offices, usually in the county town. For the North Riding of Yorkshire they were in

Layout of a scheme at Borrowby Banks.

Northallerton; for County Durham they were in Durham City. The business of administrating this drainage grant system was in the hands of drainage officers. There was a chief drainage officer, and under him six or seven area drainage officers (ADOs).

The ADOs assumed great power. As government agents who were paying 50 per cent of the cost they had overall responsibility for the design of the scheme, supervising the work and being satisfied that it was to a high enough standard before authorising payment of any grant monies.

When applying for a grant-aided drainage scheme the farmer firstly had to submit a proposal plan to the local ministry offices. In the years up to the early 1960s only the ADOs could draw up a proposal plan; from then on it was left to the farmer to use a person of his choice. Anybody could do this work provided they had the required knowledge of what was required. Not many farmers had this knowledge. A farmer could bring in an agent or consultant who would survey the field and draw up the plan, or he could still use the Ministry of Agriculture. He would need to know how much land a given size of pipe could drain.

In the post-war era all laterals used 3-inch pipes and the mains 4-inch pipes, the general assumption being that a 4-inch main could drain 25 acres, but that depended on how much fall the drain had. If it was very flat or there was more than 25 acres, a 6-inch pipe would be needed. By the start of the 1970s, ADOs stopped drawing proposal plans and it was a left to the farmer to do it himself or appoint somebody on his behalf.

The simplest form of scheme was a 4-inch main drain up one side of the field and 3-inch laterals at right angles to it across the major slope. If the field was flat from one side to the other then the angle of the laterals could be swung uphill to give some fall on them. Some fields had a slight hill in the middle, in which case a main up each side was needed. Laterals could be drawn straight across the field, the fall changing at the high point, or they could be broken and swung slightly uphill. The third type would be where a field had its low place in the centre, in which case it would need a main in the low place and laterals feeding in from both sides. Lateral spacing was not as close as it had been in some of the older schemes, where they went up and down the slope. Nevertheless, these schemes were known as close spaced schemes, with laterals spaced at 15 to 30 yards, but not less than 15 yards. The average for this area was 18 to 22 yards, and we once drew a scheme up at 25-yard spaces but it was rejected on the grounds that if the farmer then applied to have intermediate ones put in at a later date, that would bring them down to 12½ yards, which they would not pay a grant on. So that scheme was redrawn at 30-yard spaces.

All drainage outfalls into an open ditch had to have a headwall. In the early years this was a wall built around the outfall pipe in the bank of the ditch using engineering bricks.

The later precast concrete headwall showing the vermin grate fitted to the salt-glazed outlet pipe.

A vermin grate had to be fitted to the end of the pipe, which had to be salt-glazed or a sanitary type, then a splash plate had to be laid in the ditch bottom to prevent the water coming from the outfall wearing a hole in the bottom of the ditch. During the 1960s, precast concrete headwalls became available, which saved several man hours. Some schemes called for an inspection chamber, which again in the early years were rectangular, brick-built structures with 3-foot by 2-foot internal dimensions. The precast concrete ones, which again became available in the mid 1960s, were circular, with the bottom section built of brick. Inspection chambers had to have a silt trap in the bottom of at least 6 inches below the outlet pipe. A circular concrete slab was laid in first; bricks were then laid in circular fashion, similar to building a well.

These were usually laid dry, two or three courses to the pipe bottom, and then bricks were used to fill in around the pipes up to a level where the concrete rings could be used. These were 2 feet 6 inches internal diameter and 12 inches deep, and two or three rings were needed for normal depth work. Some schemes called for an underground junction box. These were very much simpler structures, with a slab on the bottom and another on the top, otherwise

built up of brick, usually without mortar.

The other type of scheme was a tile-cum-moling scheme. Laterals in the early years in the North Riding would be laid at 3 chains (66 yards) apart, which was brought down to 2 chains in later years. Durham, on the other hand, was quite happy with 4 chain spaces. Having laid the pipes, the trench then had to be filled to within 12 inches of the surface with permeable fill, usually coarse gravel. When the soil backfilling had been

A precast concrete inspection chamber.

The layout of a scheme at Killerby.

completed the field was mole drained at right angles to the laterals. There were strict rules about moling: 21 inches deep, 3 inches diameter mole and a maximum of 8 feet between moles. Tile-cum-moling schemes were appreciably cheaper in the early years of 3- or 4-chain spacing, but at 2 chains, the saving was only marginal. Conditions had to be right and there was a recommendation to re-mole every ten years.

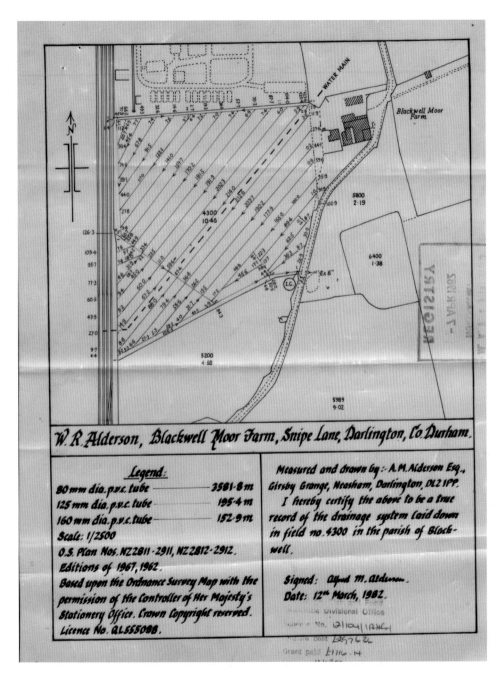

W. R. Alderson, Blackwell Moor Farm, Snipe Lane, Darlington, Co. Durham.

Legend:
80 mm dia. p.v.c. tube ———————— 3581·8 m
125 mm dia. p.v.c. tube ————————— 195·4 m
160 mm dia. p.v.c. tube ————————— 152·9 m
Scale: 1/2500
O.S. Plan Nos. NZ 2811 - 2911, NZ 2812 - 2912.
Editions of 1967, 1962.
Based upon the Ordnance Survey Map with the
permission of the Controller of Her Majesty's
Stationery Office. Crown Copyright reserved.
Licence No. QL555098.

Measured and drawn by: A. M. Alderson Esq.,
Girsby Grange, Neasham, Darlington, DL2 1PP.
I hereby certify the above to be a true
record of the drainage system laid down
in field no. 4300 in the parish of Blackwell.

Signed: Alfred M. Alderson.
Date: 12th March, 1982.

The ADOs liked to think they wielded great power; they were responsible for approving the proposal plan and then supervising the work as it was being done. If somebody else had drawn up the proposal plan they were supposed to check that it was workable before approving it, and sometimes they would refer it to the chief. They had to be notified three days before the work commenced. Then they visited as little or as often as they wished. In our early years, in fact, most of the time that I was involved with it, we were not allowed to backfill until they had seen the work. This caused problems, particularly where permeable backfill had to be used because trench sides would collapse while waiting for this inspection.

One of Alf Alderson's final record plans, dated 1982, with metric measurements.

After completion of the scheme the whole thing had to be accurately measured and a final record plan drawn up. The final record had to drawn on tracing linen and a paper copy given to the farmer and, of course, one to the contractor, from which he could make out his bill. One person who specialised in this work was WO's cousin, Alf Alderson. His plans were exceedingly neat and he spent long hours measuring schemes before drawing the final record plan. He used a 100-foot tape, carried in a box with a ring on each end. He then made some pegs with rings at the top, which fitted through the rings on the ends of the tape. As he was measuring the length of a drain he would secure one end of the tape and then start walking along the drain. He carried a home-made pulley, which the tape ran around. As he reached 100 feet, he secured this end of the tape with another peg into the ground, and then gave the tape a tug, which was sufficient to uproot the first peg, and off he went again feeding the tape around his pulley. Length of drain, distance from the next drain and distance from 'a permanent feature' all had to be measured and recorded on the final record plan. Sometimes it was difficult to find a permanent feature, particularly if hedges and trees were being removed at the same time.

The final plan was meant to be as close as possible to the proposal plan. If some changes needed to be made while the job was in progress the Ministry had to be informed. One day, I was setting up for a trencher in a field on the side of the A19 road. The plan showed five laterals at 15-yard spaces but when it came to setting the drains out, I couldn't get five in. I couldn't get four in at 15 yards; I could only get three in. The local ADO had drawn this plan up from the comfort of his office using an old Ordnance Survey map, which didn't show that land had been taken from this field for the widening of the A19 some years earlier.

Land drainage was and still is one of the best investments a farmer can make. A scheme was installed on this farm some 40 years ago, with an inspection chamber under a hedge. If I am walking on that part of the farm I often go near to this chamber and can hear water falling into it. There has been a lot of money spent over the years on this farm on gleaming new tractors and combines, most of which have now been assigned to the scrapheap, but that drainage system keeps on going as well as it did 40 years ago.

One evening in my young farming days, I was asked to give a short talk on land drainage, and in the question session that followed I was asked if it was possible to overdrain. The answer, of course, is no: drainage improves the soil structure, allowing plants to form a better root system with which they can find moisture in droughty periods. Anybody who has ever had to dig a hole in a field in very dry conditions knows that the hardest place to dig is one that is wettest in winter; waterlogged conditions destroy the soil structure and it sets like concrete.

The English Fens, once drained, have very fertile soil, which is similar to the situation prevailing in Holland. In fact, a lot of the expertise used in draining the Fens originally came from Holland. The Dutch have a saying that 'God made the world but the Dutch made Holland'. Much of Holland is like the English Fens – very flat and low-lying. The fields are divided by open ditches, totally straight, with under drains running across them, with their own outfall into these ditches. The iconic image of the Dutch landscape is a flat land with windmills dotted all over it. The image is symbolic of the work that Dutch people put into making a very rich and fertile agricultural economy.

It is not only the Fens that have problems with low-lying land, very close to sea level. There are parts of Yorkshire, albeit on a much smaller scale, where artificial means of drainage are required. The most northerly of the Yorkshire rivers, the Swale, and its tributary, the Wiske, have areas of low-lying land on either side of them. The Wiske internal drainage board do a good job of maintaining the ditches and watercourses that feed the Wiske. Many of them have little or no gradient and need

An Archimedean screw at Maunby lifting water into the river Wiske.

regular attention. Some of this land is as low as the bottom of the watercourse so in order to drain these fields some method of elevating water up 2 or 3 feet is needed. This can be a simple submersible pump or, in many cases, an auger laid in a trough at 45 degrees – known as an Archimedean screw – is sufficient to raise water from one stream to a higher one.

This may all sound very elaborate, but it has transformed large areas from being very poor, rough grazing into good, fertile arable land.

The 'engine house' of the Archimedean screw. There are three sensors in the water that start or stop the main motor, driving the auger as and when required. There is a second smaller motor driving a grease pump, which forces grease down to the phosphor bronze bearing at the bottom of the auger permanently running submersed.

Twin submersible pumps installed at Ainderby Steeple, lifting water about 6 feet in order to flow into the river Swale.

Back to the Story

The new Howard Super trencher, equipped with Roadless four-wheel drive, began work in January 1961. By that time Fords were selling the 'Super' Major, but this trencher was built around a 'Power' Major. It had the Perkins 4/270 engine of 65 horsepower. One peculiarity was that the throttle handle worked the opposite way around to the ones with Ford engines. It had two extra pieces in the transmission, one being the Howard reduction box, and the other the Roadless transfer box for the four-wheel drive. Those two pieces meant that the driver was a long way from the steering wheel. The clutch and brake pedals were in the normal place, so it wasn't possible to move the seat forward. Most of the time I used to drive it from a standing position, but this wasn't always possible.

A Howard Super trencher working from behind.

The first job it went to was a tile-cum-moling scheme of 60 chains. The laterals had to have gravel backfill but we had no equipment to do this, not even a loader. So we sub-let that job back to the farmer who, with help from his sons, did the job by hand using a tractor and trailer. The trencher performed well, but with it being new to us many things had to be learnt and the job took about two weeks in total. We then went on to do another two jobs. We were using the tile layer but one man was needed for that, and a driver. That was two men, and some days we had a struggle to find two. Our other contracting activities were taking up all available manpower. The thresher was working every day. There was quite a bit of ploughing and it was an early spring, which brought a bigger than normal demand for rotavating. Mother had a cousin who came on a part-time basis to drive the trencher, but it was clear that to get the best out of that machine we would need more staff with it.

In spring of that year we did another tile-cum-moling scheme, but again we had no equipment for this. We hired a local farmer with his tractor, loader and trailer. I went with him to help shovel the gravel into the trenches, which convinced me that a side discharge gravel trailer was an absolute necessity.

The tile layer on the Howard was not performing well. The problems were caused by the way the trencher lifted, pivoting around the front shaft. As it became shallower, crumb would creep under the toe of the crumber before it resumed its correct position. As you looked back along the drain you could see places where pipes were raised with crumb underneath them. These pipes had to be lifted and the crumb scooped out. This was quite a worry because not only was it time-consuming but there was also a danger that some places may not be detected and this would restrict the flow of water in that lateral. So by the autumn of that year we took the decision to stop using the tile layer and to lay the tiles by hand. The first part of the hand tile laying was to clean the crumb out of the trench using either a 4- or 6-inch scoop. Then a small amount of water was poured into

the trench and the bottom scooped again. This was done with a 3- or 4-inch scoop with a horseshoe attachment and a long shaft. These scoops were always pushed along the trench while standing on the surface beside the trench. In the early years this was Walter Robson's job. His brother, Eddie, followed up with the tile hook laying tiles. One thing that was very noticeable as we laid pipes in this way was how uneven the trench bottom was. It would not have been possible to lay tiles on this trench bottom without scooping it first. The pneumatic tyres were responsible for this, allowing the machine to bounce as it was working.

The 3-inch drain tiles weighed approximately 2 tons per thousand. On wet ground, tractors – which were all two-wheel drive – had difficulty pulling trailers loaded with drain tiles. So, in the autumn of 1961, I made a transport box that held 300 3-inch drain tiles, and this carted all the tiles to that machine for several years. Early in 1962, after two or three jobs of getting water from wherever possible to test the drains, we built a water bowser. It had a cylindrical 120-gallon tank saved from an old War Ag fuel trailer and was built onto an angle iron frame. The drawbar connected in the conventional way for that time, with a flat bar with a hole in it for the drawbar pin. We built a hook that stood about a foot above the drawbar and a horizontal bar was then constructed under the transport box. Then the tractor could pick up the bowser and move it short distances.

There weren't too many comforts around when draining; there was no farmhouse with a large burning fire to have your dinner in. Nor at that time did we always have vans or Land Rovers on site. So in early 1962 we bought a wooden hut, which became our site hut. It had a seat along one side and we fitted a drop-down table at the other side, where four men could sit comfortably and eat their meals out of the wind and rain. It locked up so we kept our tools and other ancillaries there. Also, a copy of the plan for that job was pinned up in the hut. It was less than a month old when, on returning to work at a site near

The Hale Gravel Backfill trailer.

Billingham on the Monday morning after a stormy weekend with gale-force winds, we were greeted by the sight of the hut blown over and up onto its roof. We managed to get it upright but its corner joints were very slack, so we manufactured some diagonal steel strips to firm it up again.

In 1962 we eventually got round to buying a side discharge gravel trailer. It was manufactured by John Salmon from Essex. It had a rectangular hopper tapering down to a rubber belt which extended out three foot clear of the wheels to the right hand side. It had 12.5 X 15 tyres which were quite the widest trailer tyres of that day, but they still were not big enough. There was

The John Salmon side discharge trailer.

a notice on the front of the trailer saying maximum load 4 ton. It was only some time later when we were doing a job only three miles from a gravel quarry that we decided to collect the gravel direct from the quarry, only then did we discover that it was in fact carrying six ton.

The Fordson Major tractors did struggle with this trailer, those tractors were always considered to be heavy on their front wheels but the Salmon trailer could make them rear up. Laterals had to be gravelled right to the main and right up to the hedge, this inevitably entailed some reversing with all kinds of problems of trailer wheels sinking or tractor wheels getting into drains, the biggest relief came when the PTO was put into gear and gravel began falling into the trench.

We bought a MIL Master loader at the same time to work in conjunction with the Salmon trailer. It was fitted to a tractor with live hydraulics, and was the type with only a mechanical bucket trip. The demise of the loader came some years later, we had fitted a blade to it for backfilling and one day somebody was backfilling on a hard frost, when the loader arms cracked through behind the bucket.

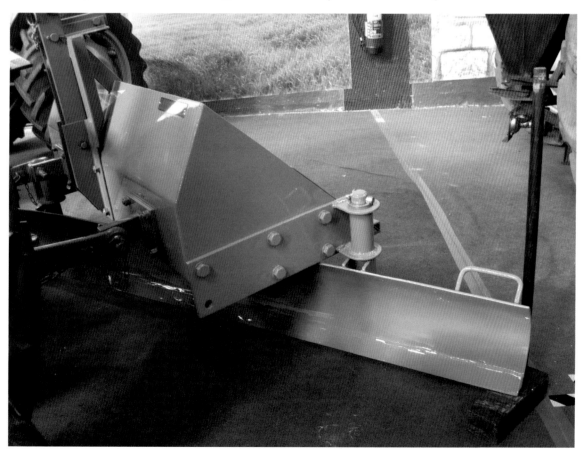

The Patterson earth scoop with grader blade fitted.

Backfilling was something that would haunt us for the first ten years of drainage. We had owned a Patterson earth scoop for several years before starting drainage work. This fitted to the three point linkage of a Fordson Major and faced backwards. We bought a Patterson grader blade which was available to be fitted under the earth scoop. There were several positions that this blade could be fitted. Two brackets bolted to the side of the scoop in a variety of ways; they could be fastened so that the blade sockets were both at the back of the scoop, the blade could then either face backwards or forwards. The brackets could also be fastened one forward and one backwards so that the blade was at an angle to the direction of travel. This was tried first without any real success the blade simply rode up over the soil. Placing it straight across and pushing backwards worked to an extent but the tractors tyres were on the wrong way round and would just stand and spin. Putting the blade the other way round, so that the tractor reversed up to the trench and then pulling the spoil into the hole as it drove forward, worked fairly well and quite a bit of work was done in that way. In wet conditions we used to change the tractor on to spade lug wheels, it would then push the blade backwards, and this was quite successful in wet conditions. The trouble was that pushing the soil in, a blade full at a time was a slow and lengthy procedure. When estimates were submitted for drainage schemes the price for trenching and tile laying included backfilling, we only allowed a very small amount for backfilling, so there was always pressure to get that job done as quickly and cheaply as possible.

What we wanted was a device on a tractor which could drive along backfilling as it went. The problem was the ADO's insistence that they inspected the work before backfilling. This caused an inevitable delay which in some cases could be up to a week. There was sure to be rain in that period allowing the spoil heap to get wet and stick together. The War ag had used a Leeford side blade on a Fordson Major with some success, but they were backfilling the same day that it was dug out. We tried a Leeford blade of our own but it couldn't cope with this wet spoil heap, the tractor simply turned to face the heap.

WO then had the idea that some mechanical means of breaking this heap up before moving it across would be worth a try. The first thing we tried was the transmission of an E27N Major tractor turned through 90 degrees then fitting a spade lug wheel to the half shaft on the ground. Three point hitch points were made for the front of it and a PTO shaft fabricated. The idea was to drive down astride of the spoil heap and this spade lug wheel would move the heap to one side and into the trench. I tried it on a Nuffield tractor, the first comment would be that it was a serious weight, the tractor badly needing some front end weight. The tractor astride of the spoil heap meant that one wheel was right on the trench side, if it wasn't the front wheel in the drain it was the back one. And the same problem existed, that is to say that in moving a quantity of earth sideways, there is considerable sideways pressure on the tractor, and with only the tractor tyres providing the resistance, the tractor would always want to turn. So after several attempts without success that machine was committed to the scrap heap.

A contractor friend of WO in Lincolnshire who he had met through the contractors association had a backfilling machine manufactured by Barth Holland. This contractor would have liked to sell this machine, but to begin with he encouraged us to take it on trial. We sent a lorry down to the Boston area to collect this machine. This was an auger on the three point linkage but it was set up in such a way that the tractor wheels had to be set out to their widest setting and the tractor then drove astride of the spoil heap and the trench. This auger ran in such a way that the soil was thrown forward and across in the direction of the trench. I believe that like the Leeford blade this machines would have worked satisfactorily in newly dug spoil, but in solid wet material it would ride over it and then turn the tractor with a front wheel into the drain. So that machine was returned to its owner.

The Leeford blade was fine when fitted to a County tractor but a Fordson Major was never up to the job.

There was yet another attempt to make a mechanical backfilling machine, this one involved an old bolt on rotavator. The blades were taken off and the direction of drive was reversed, then an auger was constructed around the rotor. It was probably the nearest we had come to an effective back filling machine, but it wasn't good enough
the tractor front wheel was continually being forced into the drain, we tried it several times but eventually gave up and scrapped it. That was our last attempt at mechanical back filling.

From then on we used a succession of blades, the Leeford side blade, the blade on the Mil Master loader, then Leeford and Bomford mule dozers.

We did not have a hydraulic digger in the early sixties but we occasionally got jobs that the Howard trencher couldn't do. One job in particular springs to mind in December 1962 there was about 15 chain of 6" main that was too deep for the trencher going as deep as seven foot. We hired in a local contractor who had a new JCB 4. The ground was quite wet and that machine could not move itself anywhere, after being towed to the drain it then had to help itself along the drain by pushing with its back actor bucket. On both sides of the trench there were deep ruts left by this machines wheels. The clay subsoil was dry and very hard and this machine appeared to be extremely slow, from which we were convinced that when the time came to buy a digger it would be some make other than JCB.

1963 began with twelve weeks of frost and deep snow. It was wonderful draining in those conditions, the land was firm, the snow kept ones boots clean and it was generally a trouble free time. We had by this time gathered up a massive amount of work, one job that came in for February was a farmer who just wanted trenches digging, then he and his farm staff would lay the pipes. We were working on a substantial job north of Teesside, which the trencher worked on from Monday to Friday, then on Friday evening it was brought home and then had two

days trenching for this other farmer, over the weekend. At that time I was only eighteen and drove that trencher home on a Friday night at five PM through Stockton High Street, which seemed to be full of Stockton Corporation double decker buses, it didn't worry me then, it might have done now.

In normal conditions we could do about twenty chain a day but very often less, but in that spring we were regularly doing over thirty chain and on those weekends just trenching we could do up to fifty chain. The problem came when the frost came out, the land became very sticky and soft. One of the problems with the four wheel drive trencher was keeping it straight. The machines on rotapeds were fitted with steel front wheels with a deep rib around them to prevent them slipping sideways. The construction of the Howard was such that the digging wheel was offset to the left and the mouldboard was on the right, these two factors were supposed to keep the draft of the machine central. On the Super trencher with the soil spinner there was very little draft from the mouldboard so the machine always had a tendency to creep to the left. In greasy conditions the pneumatic front tyres couldn't hold the line, consequently the machine was progressing along the drain with its front wheels in the right hand lock. In soft conditions we often ran up and down the line with the tractor and transport box several times till we had some ruts for the trencher front wheels to run in. This was the best way of keeping it straight, otherwise it was all over the place. We did a job at Northallerton in a field that ran next to the first row of houses in the town. The main drain had to go up the side of the field next to the garden fences, it was greasy and the machine wandered and weaved from side to side, but eventually I got to the top although I would be the first to admit it was not a pretty sight. The next morning there was an angry phone call from the local ADO, who said try to keep that machine straight. We knew that he had not been to the field so questioned him on how he knew about it. He replied "it's at the end of the chief's garden and he's playing hell."

Keeping straight was only part of the problems with the Howard, the other serious problem was with stones. As soon as it began to rub against a stone the blades would bend and then start rubbing on the scraper. There had been various suggestions put to us to help this stone problem, one was to take half of the blades off, this was to give it a better chance of getting a blade under a stone rather than just rubbing against it. The other thing was slanted blades, where the blade was cut at an angle and special weld on tips were made to run at this angle. Neither helped very much at all, it may have improved it a little in a field where there were only occasional stones but in a bad field, which was full of them, it seemed to be no help at all. In order to weld straight tips on there was a small anvil supplied with the trencher, the blade was laid over it and the tip laid on at the correct angle. This anvil could also be used to straighten a bent blade by laying the blade on the anvil and then striking it with a heavy sledge hammer.

In this area we soon got to know where the stones would be, to the West lay the Pennines and the land running up to them was all full of stone. On the other hand to the South East is the North Yorks Moors but there was very little stone right up to the base of them. In April 1963 we started a job of about 200 chain on the road leading up to Scotch Corner. We expected stone but had underestimated the quantity. This job was to prove to be the last job for that machine in our ownership. It was a field on quite a slope with mains up both side of it, and laterals running across from one main to the other. The trencher had needed help from the winch to get up these mains, with constant stops and lifting out to dig stones out. Having got those laid, we then started to put laterals across the bottom. We managed four laterals but the stone problem was getting worse as we got further up the hill. So at that point we were beat with it and had to admit defeat.

Two brothers named Ken and Les Clark were doing drainage work in the Stokesley area using homemade trench ploughs.

What they consisted of was two substantial box section beams 10'-12' long and a skid pan across the front. The thing that did the digging was not unlike a digger bucket, 18" wide at the top tapering down to 8" at the bottom. At the front it was 2' 6" deep with a curved bottom and then a deflector plate above the beams. This device was then moved across the field by a substantial winch, the bucket cut into the earth and as it moved along the soil was forced up through the beams and deposited at one side of the trench. We looked at one of these, it looked a very simple device that we thought we could make, the Clarks had no objections to us copying their design.

We bought some second hand steel, among which was some 8"X4" channel which was welded together to make 8" box sections. There was a large quantity of ¼" plate from which we cut the curved side plates and the tapered bucket bottom. When all this was welded together we were ready to go and try it. Our old Lainchbury winch would never be able to pull this thing but WO knew of the existence of an Oliver 90 tractor with a Hendon winch. He bought this tractor and we towed it home and were able to get it started and running.

It had several problems but we were able to do improvised repairs sufficient to try it on this trench plough. It was recommended that we use two snatch blocks to slow the speed of the plough down. The winch rope left the winch went to one skid of the trench plough, round a snatch block and back to the tractor. The second snatch block was fastened to the tractor drawbar which the rope went round before heading back to the other skid of the trench plough. We tried to use it, but it would not pull itself into the ground, simply dragging along at approximately ploughing depth. It was then taken back to the workshop, a length of 2" shaft was cut off at an angle and then welded to the bottom of the bucket. This shaft extended in front of the bucket bottom and was slightly inclined downwards, the idea being that it would pull this machine deeper into the earth. A few other minor modifications were done before going back to the field for another try. It was very much as before with it still not going in deep enough. We put some weight on the back (including two men) and it did then start to go down, as it got down to two foot the Oliver was working harder, but then it would hit a stone and ride out onto the top again. After persevering for most of the day we finally gave up with it, we were making a mess and it was never going to be a long term solution.

The Howard machine was little over two years old but some movement in the digging wheel bearings was becoming apparent, we knew from other contractors that the bearings and spur gears in the centre of the wheel only had a limited life. We had never had the wheel apart and we were not keen to start on it now. So with all the problems we were having we began talking to Preston Farmers about the possibility of replacing the Howard with a new Allen trencher.

As part of this process we went over to Preston, where the sales manager took us to see an Allen working. When we arrived at the field the contractors had just got the machine set in to a long lateral, after a short discussion, they were ready to start but this contractor insisted that I get onto the seat and drive it. It was quite different to
driving the Howard, the steering was most noticeable if the sighting upright on the front of the machine was deviating a slight touch on the steering brakes brought into line immediately. The grading appeared to work well and the tile layer was being used without problems. The contractor warned that stones could be a problem, what he was referring to was stones in a bucket becoming jammed against the scraper at the top. We felt that unlike the Howard with its L shaped blades at least the Allen ones were U shaped buckets bolted at both sides and would stand considerably more contact with stones before bending.

So we made the decision to change the Howard machine for

a new Allen 9/15 drainage Trencher. The new machine was delivered on 3rd May 1963 to a different job from the one we had abandoned some time earlier. It performed well with no problems, we then hired somebody with a motorised low loader to move it back to our earlier site. We soon knew what that Lancashire contractor meant about stones jamming in the scraper. It was possible to reverse the wheel to free the stone but we found that a handy sledge hammer would deal with them as the scraper was right beside the driving position. Bigger stones were difficult to get up out of the ground, slowing the wheel down and giving it time would often work but in extreme cases the machine would have to be lifted out and the stone dug out by hand.

Hiring in a low loader was obviously an additional cost that could be saved if we had our own tractor drawn low loader. Whilst I was working on this second job WO found a trailer, which, with some modification might make a suitable low loader. We were never sure what this trailer had been used for previously, it was obviously some kind of military application, when we got all the unnecessary parts off it down to its chassis, there was a circular formation in the centre. It could have carried a gun or a search light we will never know. It had knock out axles both front and rear, single 10.5X16 back tyres and 900X16 fronts. At the front the chassis narrowed in to approximately two foot and in between a large leaf spring with a pin through it, before it went on to support the front axle. So this was the basis of our first low loader. It needed a good strong front cross member and some side frame members and a floor. The cross member was fabricated flush with the chassis and steel chequer plate used for the floor, the side rails were 5"X5" angle iron spaced so that the trencher tracks only had an inch of movement between them. We always removed the front axle, there was only the one pin to remove then it could be pulled clear by the tractor, which was also used to push the axle back. The trailer could then be lowered to the ground and the trencher driven onto it. It was hard work jacking it back up again with the trencher on but we never had any trouble with it and it was used for several years. It was quite a load for the tractors of that time and sometimes we used two Fordson Majors pulling in tandem. On one occasion I was moving it with a Nuffield and had to go up Chapel bank at Worsall, the first gear change that I made was from fifth to fourth, I should have gone for third, it didn't have enough power for fourth so I had to make a second change. By that time I had lost all forward momentum so I had to set off from a standing start when one wheel simply started to spin on the road, this was a bit of a problem which called for drastic action, so I stood up on the diff lock pedal, when it engaged the tractor bounced a little and then slowly set off.

We were never short of drainage work, often short of men and sometimes short of tractors. Moling schemes accounted for only a small percentage of our work but nevertheless there was always mole draining to be caught up on. We had a Ransomes mounted mole drainer, most makes of mole drainers whether they were trailed or mounted relied on a skid to follow the ground and a blade which passed through the skid and was pinned to the skid at the required depth. The Ransomes one did not have a skid, it had a long mole about two foot long and three inches in diameter which kept its depth and floated on the tractors linkage. We liked this system because if it encountered a bump in the field it went through it slightly deeper maintaining the gradient of the mole whereas a skid would ride over the bump lifting the mole with it. The ADO's could not get their heads around this concept but kept on insisting that having a skid was the only way to mole drain.

The mounted mole drainer was fitted to the linkage of the Fordson Major but it took two tractors to pull it and very often one of them needed to be on spade lug wheels. Grandfather had retired so we had the use of the International WD6 which had been WO's first threshing tractor. We had a 25 acre mole draining job on the road side to do. There were some good spade lugs for the WD6 so we used that on front of a Fordson Major. A condition of the grant approved schemes was that the ADO be informed when the moling was to take place. Eddie Robson drove the Major and I drove the WD6, which was higher geared than the Fordson, I was in first gear and Eddie was in second and at that, they were very well matched for speed, and everything was going well until we saw a maroon Ford Anglia parked in the gateway.

This was the local ADO and everything was wrong for him; we still hadn't fitted a skid (we had no intention of fitting one) we had no expander behind the mole, the specification called for a three inch mole, most machines had a two inch mole with a three inch diameter expander behind it, but the Ransomes had a three inch mole, the expander was four and a half inch diameter, which we would never have pulled. Then we were travelling too fast, so Eddie had to change into first gear and I cut the throttle back to half way on the International, until such time as the Anglia drove away, when normal service resumed.

We did however recognise that mole draining was a problem to us, at one time in that year we hired a Caterpillar D2 to go on the front of the Fordson Major, it performed very well although only a small crawler. Later in the summer we bought a second hand County Crawler with bulldozing equipment. Again that was just used on the front of a wheeled tractor but mole draining although needing two men was less of a problem.

One afternoon we moved the Allen into a job in County Durham, the outfall was into a rather large ditch. I set the sight poles up and lowered the digging wheel into the ditch and began trenching, I only went about ten yards enough to allow the men to fit the headwall and pipe up to the tile layer. At that point it was our finishing time so we left for the day. The following morning we were surprised to find six Electricity Board vans in the field with men working near the trencher. We had apparently cut through an underground electricity cable, we knew that there was a pylon line running overhead but I had no idea that it would have an additional wire underground. One of the men said "You've had half of Darlington cut off all night, we had to get a helicopter up to locate the problem".

In the summer of 1963 the North Riding war ag finally closed the Northallerton depot. There was an auction sale on the premises which we went to. Quite a few other counties were still operating and much of the Northallerton equipment was transferred to other depots. There was one Priestman Wolf with dragline in the sale, their two Howard trenchers had gone elsewhere two Fordson Majors were sold and their last crawler with bulldozer a Fowler Challenger 3 was also sold that day.

After we bought the County Crawler we were surprised by how much work came in for it, hedge and tree removal, ponds to fill in as well mole draining. The problem was that this particular model was completely clapped out. It kept loosing a track off, its steering brakes were largely ineffective and it gave no confidence to take onto a job of any size. The answer would have been to replace it with a new bigger crawler. This would have represented a considerable capital outlay we had just bought the Allen a few months earlier. Nevertheless we looked at crawler tractors the two that were of most interest were the International BTD 8 or the Track Marshall 70. Things were further complicated because we knew that we needed a hydraulic digger for the ditching, deep digging and jobs with excessive stone. Preston Farmers had a Shawnee Warrior excavator in stock that had only done 300hrs it was mounted on a Nuffield tractor and seemed to be entirely suitable for our needs. After much deliberation we had also concluded that the Track Marshall would be more suitable than the International, Preston farmers were now agents for Track Marshall. The dilemma was that we would not be able to do both, but which one to choose.

For the first six months with the Allen things went very smoothly. It was after this that we began to have trouble with the tracks. As I have mentioned already, they were running the wrong way

round, with the slack track running along underneath. Once the sprockets began to show a little bit of wear, driving the machine forward and then using the steering brakes would bring a track off. Consequently, when not in work we always drove it backwards, so that any slack track travelled along the top. Under the heading 'The silliest thing I ever did', we did a job for a farmer who had some land over the railway line. The railway line just happened to be the East Coast main line, which at that point had four tracks – the outside two for goods trains and the centre two for the express passenger trains. Fortunately it was a long, straight length of track with good views in either direction. I simply drove the machine across the normal way because we hadn't encountered the track problems at this stage. On the way back across, the first of the central lines was about a foot higher than the outside

The Mark III Allen with Skinningrove steel works in the background.

one. As the machine climbed up onto the centre rail I looked down at the machine's track and could see all this slack track hanging down and clear of the bottom rollers. Had I made any move to correct the steering, then a track would have certainly come off. It can't be imagined the carnage there would have been if this had happened. Fortunately, it didn't, but it wasn't long after that when shedding tracks began.

In November 1963, the Contractors Association organised a tour for drainage contractors to Holland. W.O. and I went on that tour, and it was well organised and very interesting.

A Van Den Ende machine working in Holland in 1963.

Apart from visiting several farms where drainage was taking place, we also visited the polders, where recovering land from the sea was in full swing. We also spent one day in Germany, where re-aligning of flood defences was taking place. We had some of the biggest drainage contractors in England on that coach. The conversation centred on how many machines they had: some had bought two Allens a year ago and another two this year; some were employing 30 men, and some 40. It made a young lad, just two years out of school, feel very inadequate,

having only one machine and four men. After the party broke up in London the two of us travelled back to Darlington on the train, and I remember saying to W.O. on that journey, "I think tomorrow you should go to Preston's, buy that Shawnee digger and order a new Track Marshall. That made him blow his cheeks out but he didn't comment. The following evening he arrived home in the car having been to Preston's. He said, "Well, I've done what you said. The Shawnee will be here next week but it will be into January before the Track Marshall comes."

The Shawnee Warrior mounted on a Nuffield 460 tractor.

The Track Marshall mole draining with Harold Barker in the driving seat.

The Shawnee duly arrived. Its first job was with the front loader, loading the Salmon trailer with gravel on a tile-cum-mole scheme. Then it went off to start on a big scheme digging deep through a hill, for a 9-inch main, ready for the trencher when it arrived sometime later. From then on that machine was kept busy as there seemed to be ever-increasing work to the west in stony conditions.

Then, in January 1964, the new Track Marshall was delivered and the County Crawler taken away. The Track Marshall 70s came in a choice of formats: the 70C, which had a differential and steering controlled by brakes; or the 70H, which was clutch and brake steering. The 70C was the best option for field towing, ploughing and cultivation, whereas the 70H was the best for bulldozing, where the load may be at one side of the blade. The cultivation load would be from the tractor's drawbar, which was central on the tractor. When steering was required on the 70C, one track would slow down by a percentage while the other one would speed up by the same amount, giving a constant load on the tractor. When bulldozing a load at one side of the blade, for example, when digging round a tree, the controlled differential tractor would simply turn towards the tree. The same would happen when angle dozing drains in. So, whichever option was chosen, there would always be an element of compromise. On balance, we felt the clutch and brake system would best suit the work we were likely to give it.

So we went for the 70H, with two steering levers; the first movement of the lever disengaged the clutch, and further movement applied the brake to that particular track. When mole draining, only the first position was needed. In fact, it was difficult doing little enough, and there was a slight jerk to the tractor. It was, however, a good machine and ideal for our type of work. Although it was a ton heavier than the Allen trencher it could still be moved on our low loading trailer.

When the North Riding War Ag was closing down, the Divisional Executive Office of the Ministry of Agriculture sent local contractors a list of the men that were being made redundant. One of those men was Harold Barker. He had last driven the Fowler Challenger 3, but had had 20 years with the War Ag, mostly on crawler tractors, which had, prior to the Fowler, mainly been International TD9s. After we had ordered the Track Marshall, W.O. went to see Harold and successfully engaged him to begin to work driving the new Track Marshall.

I was always conscious that when working alongside Harold I was watching a craftsman at work. Everything he did was so meticulous and done to perfection. People used to say, "Don't use a bulldozer to take hedges out; you get too much soil mixed in with the thorns," but that was not the case when Harold Barker was driving. He approached the hedge first with the blade about 6 inches above the ground, struck the hedge and pushed the bushes over, which drew the nearside roots out of the ground. He would then reverse and approach again, making contact with the bottom of these overturned thorns and pushing them away, and the remaining roots would come out of the ground cleanly.

In 1964, we bought a Miles mole drainer. This was the same as the one Harold had used on the War Ag – a trailed machine with a long ground skid and hitherto steel wheels – but when we ordered this machine they offered us the option to take it without wheels, with just six stud hubs ready to take 11 x 36 tractor back wheels. We took this option because it meant that we could transport it on the road behind a tractor. We did quite a lot of moling-in of alkathene pipes for water supplies to field troughs and, in some cases, to farms. We had in the past used the tractor-mounted mole plough, very often with a winch on the front tractor giving a slow, steady pull. The Miles mole drainer was used for pipe laying, with it only needing one tractor and winch, as by now we had the Boughton HDN 2 winch, which was ideal for this type of work.

Miles Mole drainer.

There were also several scrub clearance jobs that had come in for areas that had been woodland, where the trees had been felled many years earlier, although some had been left and had become known as fox coverts. All the bushes and tree roots had to be removed and burnt, and then the land ploughed and, in most cases, drained. We bought a second-hand single furrow plough to be used with the Track Marshall. It was a Massey Harris Prairie Buster. It was a single furrow plough turning a furrow up to 2 feet wide and 12 to 15 inches deep.

The Massey Harris 'prairie buster' plough.

By the year end and into 1965, we bought a Massey Ferguson tractor/digger/loader combination. The Shawnee was draining constantly in the stonier areas and we needed another machine for ditch cleaning work. The Massey was the best for ditching; it had more than 180 degrees of slew and the bucket crowded in a much more compact arc than that of the Shawnee.

By 1965, the Shawnee was starting to show signs of severe wear. One afternoon early in that year, we were draining with the Allen when we cut a water pipe, the whereabouts of which we had not been informed. It was a 2-inch pipe that supplied one farm and six or eight houses. We managed to find a stop tap and cut off the flow of water. I went off in the van to a nearby village where there was a plumber with whom we had worked previously. He was at work but agreed to come to us in the evening. Because it was early in the year, as I arrived back at the site it was already getting dark. The Shawnee happened to be there, but had not been used on that particular day. I knew this plumber would not want to work down a 9-inch trench so I started the Shawnee and began to dig a wider hole over the burst water pipe. I had only got two bucketfuls dug when the slewing chain broke. This was a desperate situation. We had no means of repairing it, the plumber was coming and we needed to get the pipe repaired that evening. We took the cover off around the sprocket at the base of the king post and removed the chain completely. I then had an idea: as I could still dig and fill the bucket, surely we could find a way of swinging it to one side. After I had lifted the full bucket I partially lowered one side stabiliser until the bucket swung by gravity to that side. Then, after emptying the bucket, I lifted that side again and the bucket began to swing back to the centre and had to be dropped as it passed over the trench. This was the most unorthodox way of digging a hole but, with the help of tractor and van lights, the hole was dug and the pipe repaired that evening.

Durham War Ag closed their contracting operations in September 1965, and an auction sale was held on 2nd October that year. At this sale there was quite a bit of machinery that had previously been at other depots, including the Northallerton gravel trailer, a Fisher Humphries single furrow plough with a back wheel and Harold Barker's old mole plough. There were also no fewer than eight Priestman Wolf excavators. One had only a dragline jib, some only had the Teredo trenching jib and some had both jibs. We knew that our Shawnee Warrior was getting quite worn by this time, and these machines were making about £400. Although we knew nothing about Priestmans, they did look to be in reasonable condition, so we bought one. This was a 1955 machine, equipped with only the Teredo jib.

The Rope-Operated Excavator

The 1956 colour scheme of the Ruston Bucyrus machines.

The history of rope-operated excavators can be traced back to the early nineteenth century. The firm Bucyrus was one of the first companies to be associated with these machines, named after the town of Bucyrus in Ohio. As soon as steam power was a feasible source of energy there was a need for excavators. Bucyrus absorbed the Erie Company and became Bucyrus Erie. After the First World War they linked up with the British firm of Ruston and Hornsby, of Grantham in Lincolnshire, and formed a British subsidiary known as Ruston Bucyrus. In the inter-war years they built up a range of machines at their manufacturing facility in Lincoln, most of which were too big for agricultural purposes. The smaller of their machines was the 10RB, which was used in dragline form for dredging lowland rivers and drainage channels, particularly in the Fens. Ruston Bucyrus and Bucyrus Erie ran in parallel on either side of the Atlantic, with all of their machines using their own engines. They had an extensive range of engines, from a three-cylinder used in the 10RB, through four-, five- and six-cylinder ones used in the 38RB.

Early RBs had been painted green but a new, distinctive livery was adopted in 1956. The track frames, undercarriage and jib were all painted green, whilst maroon and cream were the colours chosen for the cabs.

The firm manufactured many other items of heavy plant, including hydraulic bulldozing equipment for crawler tractors, most prominently the International range of crawlers.

Other firms to be involved in the excavator market, which included the production of cranes, were Ransomes, Rapier, Smiths and NCK. These machines did not appear to have made a significant impact on the land drainage aspect of the business but did enjoy reasonable success in industrial applications.

The more successful excavator manufacturer in this country, as far as land drainage was concerned, was the all-British firm of Priestman Brothers, of Hull. The business was started by William Dent and Samuel Priestman in 1870. By 1895, cash flow problems forced the company to go into public ownership. The Priestman brothers lost their place on the board but the company continued under the Priestman name. Some members of the Priestman family continued to be employed, but not in a controlling role, and the firm continued in business right up until the 1970s. Most of the production of both Priestman and Ruston Bucyrus machines were far too big and heavy for agriculture. During the 1930s, Priestman's developed a range of machines that they named after animals: the Lion, Tiger and Panther, along with the smaller Wolf and Cub. The first of these to come onto the market was the Cub, in 1932. By the late 1930s, the Cub was in widespread use in agricultural draining and ditch cleaning. The larger machines, Lion, Tiger and Panther, followed soon after and by 1937, the Wolf came onto the market. The weight of the Cub was 7 to 8 tons, depending on which jib was fitted, whilst the Wolf was approximately 2 tons heavier. Some of the larger machines were used on River Board work and large ditch schemes because of their much greater reach.

The civil and environmental engineering firm of Coxon Brothers, of Bedale in North Yorkshire, used two of the Priestman Lion machines. They were known by the letters LC, meaning Lion Crane. These machines differed from the smaller ones by having their operator's cab on the right-hand side. Coxon had a LC42, which weighed in at 28 to 30 tons and was equipped with a Dorman four-cylinder engine. They also had a LC51, which was on bigger tracks, had a Lister air-cooled, six-cylinder engine, and weighed approximately 38 tons.

The Priestman LC51 with dragline digging out a water channel for the Upper Swale drainage Board.

Steam-powered excavators were still in production in 1932, but alternatives were being offered from the early 1920s, including those with petrol or petrol/paraffin Ford or Dorman engines. By the early 1940s, Dorman and McLaren diesels became available. By the end of the war, most machines were being supplied with diesel engines. The Cub used a two-cylinder Dorman or McLaren diesel engine, whilst the Wolf had a Dorman three-cylinder engine. These two machines would dominate the British market for agricultural drainage machinery for 20 years. In 1942, the wooden cab of the Cub was replaced by a steel one, and the cab on the Wolf was changed the following year.

These machines will be best remembered for their dragline equipment but they were also available with a Teredo trench-digging jib, a crane jib or a face shovel, although the latter was not generally seen in agriculture. These machines were known to those who used them as the 'navvy'. Presumably, this name went back to the days of hand digging of drains when the men doing the work were known as navvies, as they did all the hard work.

Steam powered excavators were still in production in 1932, but alternatives were being offered from the early 1920's a petrol or petrol/paraffin Ford or Dorman engines were offered. Then Dorman or McLaren Diesels became available in the early forties. By the end of the war most machines were being supplied with diesel engines, the Cub, used a two cylinder Dorman or McLaren Diesel engine, while the Wolf had a Dorman three cylinder engine. These two machines would dominate the British market for agricultural drainage machinery for twenty years. In 1942 the wooden cab of the Cub was replaced by a steel one, while the Wolfs cab was changed the following year.

These machines will be best remembered for their dragline equipment but they were also available with a Teredo trench digging jib, a crane jib or as a face shovel, although the latter was not generally seen in agriculture. These machines were known to those who used them as the "Navvy". Presumably this name went back to the days of hand digging of drains when the men doing the work were known as navvies, as they did all the hard work.

The Priestman LC51, equipped with a drop hammer, installing wood piles to create a revetment on a watercourse in the Bedale area.

The Dorman three-cylinder engine in the Priestman Wolf.

The engine was crossover at the back of the machine with chain drive to the winch drums. There were two of these, with slightly tapering drums to make the rope coil onto them evenly. They were each powered by separate cone clutches, which were engaged by pulling on the two levers in front of the driver. They also had brakes that were activated by foot pedals, and under the driver's seat there were two short levers that could lock the brake pedals down. Drive to the tracks was by roller chain and was activated by a hand-operated clutch in front of the driver between his two winch engaging levers. He had a further lever that changed the machine from travelling to digging mode. When in digging mode this central lever, instead of engaging the tracks, engaged a pinion that ran in a ring gear on the track frame and provided the slewing arrangement.

With the rear door open the position of the engine can be seen.

The driving controls on a Priestman Wolf. Of the three levers directly in front of the driver, the left one controlled the left-hand winch clutch, the right-hand one controlled the right-hand winch clutch, and the central lever controlled the rotation of the cab when in digging mode, or forward and reverse when in travelling mode. The two small cable controls positioned on the central lever were engine throttle and stop control. The lever to the extreme left was the engine clutch, and the one high up to the driver's right was the cab lock, which prevented rotation when travelling. The two levers low down to the right controlled steering and track lock when digging.

The under gear of the tracked excavator believed to be from a Ruston, Priestmans were very similar. This shows the dog clutches on which partial movement would disengaged the drive for steering corrections, further movement would lock the disc onto a projection which would lock the tracks. Both tracks could be locked from the cab to hold the machine when digging.

The tumbler sprocket driving the cast pads of the Priestman

For steering the machine while travelling a system known as 'spragging' was deployed. This involved stopping the forward or reverse motion of the machine and then disengaging the drive to one or other of the tracks. The drive to the tracks consisted of a vertical shaft that went down through the central ring gear to a gearbox, from where two shafts ran to each side of the machine, with sprockets that drove the chains that powered the tracks. Within the length of these shafts were dog clutches. When turning, one of these clutches would be disengaged, allowing the track to stop and the machine to turn. In some cases there were also pins, which as the dog clutch was disengaged slid out and entered a hole in a disc, ensuring a positive stop to that track. After the correction had been made to the steering the spragging device was withdrawn, and the machine could then carry on travelling.

An early Priestman Cub, with a wooden cab.

The driving position on the Priestman Cubs and Wolfs was in the front left-hand corner of the machine. On RBs and others, including the bigger Priestmans, it was on the right-hand side. The driver's seat was a saddle similar to that of a motor cycle; he was constantly using the brake pedals straight below him and this had been found to be the most comfortable type of seat. The whole machine was then encased by the cab. The entry door was on the left-hand side behind the driver. The cladding then carried on to the back and across the back to where there was another door in the back right-hand corner. The cladding then continued along the right-hand side and across the front to where the ropes travelled out to the jib. It was always warm working in that cab, and rather noisy. It was possible to walk

around the engine and all the winching mechanism to the front right-hand corner, where there was a small work bench with a vice. This was to enable the driver to repair his wire ropes should the need arise. Most Priestmans in the wooden cab and early steel cab eras were painted green, but they offered orange paint as far back as the late 1940s, and, furthermore, they offered to paint machines in any colour of the customer's choosing. All War Ag machines were painted green.

There was a further control, which was the derricking gear. This was an additional small winch situated within the machine, the rope from which controlled the angle of the jib. When the dragline was being used the jib would be held in position by the

The Wolf, with Teredo digging equipment.

derricking rope and the lifting rope would run up the jib, over a pulley and down to the bucket. The bucket was quite a long affair and very heavy, so that it could be pulled by a rope to the top and remain flat. The bucket would usually have a pulley, which the digging rope went round before going back to the frame of the machine.

Digging was done by the digging rope pulling at the bucket, with the lifting rope being allowed to be slack. At the end of the stroke the lifting rope would be activated. While keeping the digging rope tight after it was lifted and the machine slewed, the digging brake was released, allowing the bucket to tip downwards, shedding its load before the machine was swung back into position and the digging cycle started again.

A Cub VI, with the later type of side arm fitted.

Also available for use on this size of machine was the Teredo jib, for trench digging. This was a solid jib, much shorter than the dragline jib, and it had a dipper arm, not unlike the later hydraulic excavators. It was worked by the two winch drums, with the lifting rope going to the top of the dipper arm and the digging rope going to the bottom of the dipper, just above the bucket. There was a shaft at the top front of the machine with a series of pulleys on it. The lifting rope went around one pulley on this shaft, out to a pulley at the top of the dipper arm, around that, back to the machine, around another pulley and then out to the dipper again, where it was secured. The digging rope went out from the winch drum, out to the dipper bottom, around a pulley and back to the machine, where it was secured. The bucket was pivoted on the dipper at a point near the back of the bucket. At the front there were two pieces of steel going up to the jib, parallel to the dipper. This arrangement gave the bucket parallel action when digging. The bucket was about 18 inches wide at the top, tapering down to 10 inches at the bottom. With a central round tooth it made a curved bottom trench. There was an ejector paddle linked to the dipper by linkage, which cleaned the bucket out when fully extended.

When digging, the digging winch was activated to draw the bucket in towards the machine. The digging brake was then applied and the lifting winch activated to lift the bucket clear of the ground. The centre lever caused the machine to slew, and then the digging brake was released as the lifting winch continued lifting. The net result was that the dipper arm was extended, the ejector did its work and the cycle was ready to start again. For a trench 2 feet 6 inches to 3 feet deep, two digs of the bucket were normally sufficient. The bucket had a parallel action, so once the bucket bottom was level it wouldn't dig any deeper. There were several holes where the steel supports connected to the bucket, allowing the bucket angle to be altered. For finer variations to the digging depth it was necessary to alter the angle of the base plate on the bucket bottom. These were bolted onto the bucket, with several

washers between bucket and base plate, and the numbers of these washers could be varied to give different digging depths.

Another function that the Priestman could do was ditching. This needed the dragline jib and a side arm. On the early machines the side arm was secured under the cab on the left-hand side of the machine behind the driver's door. It protruded approximately 10 feet and then had a rope pulley on the end. On later machines the side arm was fixed under the main jib and could operate on either side of the machine. The jib was swung left until the far end was central over the ditch, then a tapered bucket was drawn from below the jib towards this side arm. The digging rope was fed around two fairlead pulleys on the front of the machine, out to the end of the side arm, around its pulley and then onto the bucket. The War Ag used this system of ditch cleaning very successfully. For very large watercourses or small rivers, the dragline bucket alone would be used.

In 1963, Priestman's made their first steps into the hydraulic excavator market. The Cub received a facelift and became known as the Mark VI. Its track size was increased and it had greater lifting capacity. The two-cylinder, water-cooled Dorman engine was still available or, as an alternative, a Lister three-cylinder, air-cooled engine was now offered. A variant known as the Hydrocub was available, still with the rope-operated digging and lifting functions but when used with their trenching jib, a hydraulic ram was used to tilt the bucket. The Mark VI Cub had the same capacity as the Wolf, so at this point, production of the Wolf ceased.

The year of 1964 was when Priestman's introduced their first hydraulic excavator, the Beaver. This machine was based on the Priestman Cub, using the same subframe with the same mechanical drive to the tracks, and the steering used the spragging device as had been used on earlier machines. The normal arrangement was that the winches for digging and lifting were taken out and a hydraulic pump was substituted, although not in the position that the winches had occupied, but further back, driven directly off the front of the engine crank shaft. The early Beavers used a Lister three-cylinder, air-cooled engine. In 1967 this was changed to a four-cylinder Lister, still air-cooled, or as an alternative, a Ford water-cooled, four-cylinder engine was offered. The driver's position was unaltered, but now, instead of winch clutch levers, he had hydraulic controls.

The central lever, which as with the Cub controlled slewing when digging, or forward and reverse when in transport mode, remained unchanged. On the left of this central lever was a long hydraulic lever, and two to the right of it. Priestman's hadn't adopted multifunctional levers at this stage. It was possible to have a Beaver with both the hydraulic functions and the winches for rope operations.

A Priestman Beaver on ditching work.

A Priestman Beaver with Teredo jib fitted.

A Priestman Mustang 120.

In the early 1970's Priestmans next machine was the Mustang. Their first machine was the Mustang 120 which was to be the first of a range of different sized Mustangs. The main difference here was to the sub frame and the tracks. The old mechanical drive which Priestmans had used for fifty years was discontinued in favour of hydraulic drives. The old "navvy" tracks were assigned to the scrap heap as a completely new type of track was deployed, using steel chain and driving sprockets with bolt on grousers as used on crawler tractors. Hydraulic motors attached to each driving sprocket eliminated the need for chains or any other form of mechanical drive. There was an even more

powerful engine with the Ford six cylinder engine now used. Priestmans now had a completely up to date machine which developed into a range of machines to see them through the 1970's.

The firm of Priestman had grown to be a large manufacturing company in the inter war years, they took a responsible attitude to the drivers and their training. A Priestman school was opened in Hull a mile or two away from the factory to train operators. During the second world war, when the women's land army was in operation women attended this school and were trained as

A 3RB hydraulic excavator

excavator drivers. Some of the drivers that we employed had been Priestman trained including Jim Akers, Eric Heseltine, Alan Jackson and Les Helme although Les' training was later, and confined to all hydraulic machines.

Ruston Bucyrus made a similar transition to hydraulics in the early 1960's. Their first attempt, based on the 10RB machine but simply had the winch drums and rope controls replaced with hydraulics. The same tracks and mechanical drive were retained at this stage, and it was designated the 3RB. During the life of

the 3RB Ruston adopted two lever control with multifunction levers.

By the end of the decade, the replacement for the 3RB was on the market. The first of these was the 20RBH, followed by the 15RBH and the 30RBH. These machines had the chain and sprocket tracks with bolted-on grousers, which were hydraulically driven. Alternatives to the Ruston engine became available: from Deutz, General Motors, or, the most popular in the UK, from Perkins.

Back to the Story

The Scammell coupling.

The two were attached by a Scammell coupling, an ingenious way of coupling an articulated trailer to its tractor unit from the cab of the lorry. There were two steel rails that began in front of the lorry's back axle and went backwards, curving downwards to a point clear of the mudguards. The turntable was built under the trailer, in this case the swan neck, and then there were arms on each side of the turntable, with rollers that ran up the rails on the tractor unit to where catches latched onto the trailer. As the rollers were going up the rails the two landing wheels were being lifted into the transport position. The brakes and the

lights coupled automatically; the only thing the driver needed to leave his cab for was to apply a hand parking brake on the trailer. This system had been developed by Scammell for use with light articulated trailers for British Railways. Scammell produced a three-wheeler tractor unit with this patented coupling for small, covered trailers, which were little more than vans that could be left by the train and filled or emptied while the little tractor unit was away delivering a load.

These couplings found their way onto larger lorries but the

fifth wheel arrangement was always dominant. There was a safety issue with the Scammell couplings, as the trailers had been known to uncouple on the road. So, when the plating of lorries was introduced, the Scammell coupling was quite heavily penalised by having its carrying capabilities substantially reduced. We actually bought this lorry and, over the next six months, W.O. bought no fewer than three flat York trailers of varying lengths, all with Scammell couplings. They had end boards fitted for carrying drain tiles, and provided useful storage for drain tiles on site. Any surplus could be moved elsewhere without further manhandling.

The low loader was bought with moving the Priestman in mind, but it was, of course, used to move the trencher and bulldozer. The Track Marshall could have been driven up the side of the trailer and twisted round on the wagon, but the track grousers gripped on the floor and were pulling it up, so to prolong its life we always took the rear axle out and loaded everything over the back.

The Priestman was taken straight to a job, and we managed to secure the services of an experienced, former Durham War Ag driver. It may have been regarded at the time as putting the clock back, but the Priestman could do approximately 15 chains per day as opposed to the 10 or 12 from the Shawnee. In order to get the best from it we sent two men to lay tiles behind it. Although they did have a Land Rover with them, they preferred to get into the navvies' cab to have their meals. The driver could lift his seat and turn it to face backwards; the other two could get in and sit on an oil drum each, close the door and have a comfortable lunch.

The Priestman Wolf, with Teredo jib, on land drainage work.

An early Fordson Major with trailer, carrying drain tiles.

The petrol Land Rover used by the Priestman gang.

They had a tractor with them, either with trailer or transport box, and a water bowser. We always used water when hand-scooping drains. The scoop was easier to use when wet and level grading was facilitated. In reasonably favourable conditions there was very little scooping to do, as the Teredo bucket made a round-bottomed trench that was usually nicely graded.

To anybody brought up with hydraulic excavators where the bucket is always attached to the dipper arm, the dragline concept is a difficult one to understand and accept. The idea of having a bucket supported solely on wire ropes will seem extremely restrictive and very limited in its use. That is not the case, however. An experienced operator could place that bucket exactly where he wanted it and perform extraordinary feats with it.

Jim Akers was just such an operator. He had served for more than 20 years with the North Riding War Ag, having initially been trained by Priestman's. He told me of a job that he had done as part of creating a new school playing field. This field had been built on a sloping field that had been levelled with the dragline bucket, which had meant digging into the clay at the high side of the site and swinging it round to the low side of the field. After the field was all level, ready for the grass seed, they moved on to the clay escarpment at the high side of the field, which had to have a layer of topsoil spread over it to allow grass to establish. Jim was able to do that job with the dragline bucket. He would swing the bucket full of topsoil in the direction of the escarpment and then release and lift the bucket, as it was still swinging, spreading the topsoil evenly. This was the work of a highly skilled operator, not only able to perform three functions at the same time, but also to ensure an even covering of soil on the escarpment.

Some of the schemes we undertook included laying main drains under council roads. One job I was involved with was an extensive scheme with no fewer than three crossings of a road. It was a C classified road, single track with not much traffic. On the mornings that we were to do the crossings we went for a very early start and simply drove the Allen across, trenching as it went. The crossing then had to be made up with gravel and the spoil heap removed with a bucket. We found that if it was backfilled with clay it would continue settling for months, even years, but stone, once compacted, did not. On another job, we crossed a B classified road that carried much more traffic. On that occasion we used two diggers, one doing the actual digging and depositing the spoil into the front bucket of the other. The road was dug up one half at a time, with one man operating a Stop/Go sign.

It was around this time that the Shawnee equipment was removed from the Nuffield tractor and sold, with the Boughton winch being bought and fitted to that tractor.

The Wolf at work, with Jim Akers driving, Raymond Anderson scooping the trench bottom and Phil Bainbridge laying pipes. They have a Fordson Major tractor with transport box and water cart towed under the box.

Another shot of the Wolf, this time working on snow.

Right: Les Clark's Mark IV Allen working at Great Broughton, with two lads feeding the tile layer.

The Mark IV Allen working at Crathorne, with Derek Smith driving, Ron Snaith on the tile layer and Bill Haw on the trailer.

In early 1967, the Mark II Allen trencher was sold in part-exchange for a new Mark IV. The earlier trencher had done a lot of work. Its truck rollers and sprockets had been changed many times, and it had had its trenching wheel turned so as to wear off the other side of the teeth on the segments around the wheel. Its tracks were in shocking condition and we had difficulty keeping them on. In contrast, the new machine, with the new, much bigger tracks driven from the back, was entirely different. The Ford 5000 power unit had more power than the Super Major on the earlier machine, and daily output rose accordingly.

The change in 1968 was that the Massey Ferguson digger was replaced by a Whitlock 205.

The Whitlock 205 ditch cleaning,
with Les Helme driving it

A later shot of the Track Marshall, with Miles mole drainer. Its cab was fitted in 1966.

This machine was a direct descendant of the old Dinkum Digger, but had moved on considerably. It was built onto a Ford 4000 tractor, and had hydraulic stabilisers in excess of 180 degrees of slew and a fully enclosed cab. This was a square-built cab with a fibreglass roof, which was often damaged when the machine was lifted on its stabilisers under a tree branch. The back window was in two halves, divided down the middle, and each half could be slid round to the side, opening up the whole of the back. The windows only came down to the valve block, which was in the centre, and at each side there was a considerable gap to the floor. Les Helme drove it. One day when he was working in a field near the A1 at Catterick, a car pulled up and the driver went into the field to look at this machine. It turned out that he was a salesman for JCB and was full of criticism for this competitor's machine. After a lengthy discussion he said, "Anyway, when you are digging on a wet day, what keeps your feet dry?" "Me willies," was Les's reply.

The Bedford S tractor unit was nothing but a pain. There were all kinds of problems with it, not least keeping the brakes in working order. That unit was replaced, also in 1968, with a new TK type Bedford. This also had the Scammell coupling so we could carry on using our existing trailers. This was a joy to drive in comparison, but legislation was starting to come through that signalled the end for the Scammell coupling on these larger trailers. So, only a year later, we were obliged to change to the fifth wheel type of coupling. This was achieved by replacing the Bedford lorry and Dyson trailer with a Ford D800 tractor unit and Tasker low loading trailer. The York trailers were never upgraded but just sold or scrapped.

Changeover day. The newly delivered Ford D800 lorry stands beside the Bedford before its departure.

Work continued to increase and there was great pressure, particularly on the trencher. We had been aware for some time that the output from a trencher could be increased if a digger could be made available to work alongside it. Setting a trencher into a main at the start of a lateral was not so easy, and the man fitting the junction pipe either had to work down a very narrow hole or dig it out wider by hand. If a digger had been present it would have dug the inset in advance and the junction could have been installed. Then the trencher would simply be lowered into this inset, the pipes connected to the junction, and off it would go. We never had a digger available to do this; we thought that buying a new one for this purpose was going to be far too expensive and worried about older ones breaking down. The firm of Fosters, of North Cave on Humberside, were making a lightweight digger to go on the three-point linkage of a tractor. It was a sensible looking machine, with hydraulic stabilisers and fixed stays to go from lift arm to tractor body to keep the thing rigid to the tractor. We had a Fordson Power Major with a Leeford Muledozer working with the trencher, so we bought one of the Foster diggers and fitted it to this tractor. That made quite a difference to the machines' output, as such as small matter as digging a hole for an inspection chamber was made all the easier with this digger around.

Les Clark driving his Mark IV Allen.

Rillington Depot

The Ford Transit van.

Through his involvement in the Contractors Association W.O. had met a man by the name of Richard Dottridge. He had been a chief drainage officer in the North Riding in the 1950s but had left to become managing director of a firm of drainage contractors known as White Horse Contractors Limited, from Blewbury in Berkshire. The firm had become very successful, opening up several branches in different parts of the South Midlands. In addition, they had also opened up a branch at a village called Rillington, near Malton in the North Riding of Yorkshire. In 1969, Mr Dottridge confided in W.O. that he was thinking about closing his Malton operation, and asked if we would be interested in taking it over. That business consisted of a Priestman Beaver, a Muir Hill trencher, a JCB 3 a Ford 3000 tractor, a tipping trailer and a van. The business employed eight men and had a full order book. After lengthy discussions W.O. agreed to take it on.

With the staffing level they had and the amount of work they carried out, they were obviously going to need a similar amount of machinery. The only things that we took over from White Horse Contractors were a small rented depot, which was little more than a wide verge alongside a farm track, along with a fuel tank and the tipping trailer. We decided to send the 1967 Mark IV Allen to them and ordered a new machine to replace it. Another Foster digger and Bomford angle dozer were fitted to a Fordson Power Major tractor and sent to Rillington. From time to time they also needed another Fordson Major for trailer work. W.O. had got to know of a firm in the Midlands that dealt in second-hand construction machinery, and he understood they had some Priestman Beavers for sale. So one day he travelled down to see these machines. When he arrived home that evening, he had bought not only one Beaver, but two. Both of these machines had the Lister four-cylinder, air-cooled engines, but one of them had winch drums as well as hydraulics. It had the normal hydraulic jib as well as a Teredo jib and a lattice crane jib. They were also provided with a new Ford van, which the trencher gang travelled to work in. The two Priestman drivers travelled to work in their own cars.

The Priestman Beaver, with hydraulic jib.

The Priestman Beaver, with rope-operated Teredo jib.

The foreman at Rillington, a man by the name of Alan Jackson, had been a North Riding War Ag driver, mainly driving Priestmans. They were initially sent the all-hydraulic Beaver. They had a Priestman driver, Eric Heseltine, and then, at a later date, the Wolf was sent there as well, and Alan drove this himself. There were jobs that, geographically, could have been done by either depot, and some that were done jointly between men from each depot. One such job was a large one for the River Wiske Internal Drainage Board. This included up to 2 miles of ditch cleaning and deepening, and about half a mile of piping that ditch in with 36-inch concrete pipes. This was a section where there were areas of sand and the banks of the stream were not sufficiently stable.

Concrete pipes being unloaded from a lorry.

Two Beavers: the hydraulic one digs the ditch out while the other, with crane jib, lowers the pipes into the ditch.

The spoil from the ditch had to be spread and the area reseeded, and guard fences had to be erected on both sides of the open ditch. There were crossing points to make with gates, and all other fences and hedges had to be made good and stock-proof. The Rillington Beaver did all the digging, and the crane jib was fitted to the other Beaver for lifting the concrete pipes, which were 6 feet long. Men from the home depot handled and laid the pipes, and every field drain that was crossed had to be joined in.

The Track Marshall spread the ditch spoil and filled in over the concrete pipes. At the crossing points two or three pipes were used, with retaining walls on both sides built of 9-inch concrete blocks. Then 3-inch limestone was brought in to make a hard crossing. Two of the Rillington men did the fencing, which along the open stream required two strands of barbed wire with posts at 12-foot intervals. Then men from the general contracting side rotavated and harrowed level the bare soil and sowed grass seed, before a final rolling.

Back to the Story

The new Allen trencher for the home depot was described as a Mark IVA. There was very little difference to the digging arrangement, but it was fitted to a Ford Force 5000 skid unit, with the engine power now up to 75 horsepower.

We had always been conscious of the amount of effort that was going into manually handling drain tiles. In the early years, brickworks in the York area were delivering drain tiles on four-wheeler lorries, a load being 4,000 3-inch tiles. I have known these loads be unloaded by as few as two men (one of us, plus the driver), but more usually there would be three or four in total, in which case a load of that size could be unloaded in about an hour. In the mid-sixties we began to source our drain tiles from the London Brick Company, usually from Peterborough. They were delivered by articulated lorries carrying 8,000 3-inch pipes. Obviously they took twice as long to unload as it was now a higher load, so more pipes had to be passed down to the man on the ground before he could reach them off the lorry himself. This was a big enough delay in itself, but very often tiles were being delivered to the next job for that gang, which would mean everybody leaving the site and travelling to this new location and unloading the lorry. By the time they had returned to the original site, half a day had been lost. This in itself was bad enough, but then they subsequently had to be handled over onto a trailer or transport box, taken to the trencher and then handled onto the tray on the machine.

*A pipe bogie was made in the workshop to carry a crate of drain tiles.
This one had wheels; later ones just had skids underneath.*

Tractors with live hydraulics were best suited to working with the forklifts. We had several Power Majors with this feature but in this instance a Super Major is being used to unload a lorry.

In the late 1960s, everything else seemed to be becoming palletised or containerised, so why not drain tiles? Drain tiles were not a very stable commodity; they couldn't, for example, simply be stacked on a pallet, as was the case with bricks. We experimented with steel pallets with three sides built up to contain the tiles. This was working reasonably well. The problem was that these crates occupied a full lorry whether full or empty, so getting them back to the brickworks required as much effort as bringing a load. We then tried collapsible sides on these pallets. These things had a good, strong base, then two sides, hinged at the bottom, with a link piece to hold them at the top. This link could be quickly disconnected, allowing the sides to fold flat across the base. They were made to hold four rows of pipes, so that one on each side of the lorry was the correct width of the load. This type was adopted and used successfully for several years, with each trencher gang now provided with a tractor and Cameron Gardner forklift attachment.

A bogie was made with two small wheels to tow from a bracket on either side track frame of the trencher. Subsequent bogies were made without the wheels, but just two skids that slid along the ground. A crate of tiles sat on this sledge, and the man on the tile layer could reach these pipes on his own. When the crate was empty, the trencher had to pause, and the man could manually tip the empty crate off the sledge for the forklift to replace it with a full one. The labour saved with this system was considerable. Now, when a lorry arrived to be unloaded, one man and forklift was all that was required to unload it.

In 1970, the Ministry of Agriculture decided to pay grants on subsoiling, following a grant-aided drainage scheme. Subsoiling was still a contractor's job; the 60 horsepower, two-wheel drive tractors of that era weren't good enough for subsoiling. We bought a toolbar frame for the Track Marshall. It had two subsoiling legs and the option to replace them with three root-grubbing tines. The Track Marshall was rated at 70 horsepower, which had always seemed adequate for all the work it had to do, but now with two subsoiler legs it suddenly looked underpowered, and most of the subsoiling was done in first gear. With it being grant-aided, the ADOs were able to inspect and make sure the 20-inch depth was adhered to. The majority of the scrub clearance schemes had been done by the 1970s, but there were a few small jobs that these tines were used for. The old prairie buster plough was getting terribly rough. Harold Barker said of it, "It's about as firm as a set of chain harrows." So, with the advent of these rooter tines, that plough was scrapped.

We were now running two Allen trenchers, three Priestman excavators and the Track Marshall. All were transported by the Ford low loader, which now had an allocated driver. His time was filled in by delivering fuel or sundry requisites in a van or Land Rover. There was also a full-time fitter in the workshop.

We would fairly often encounter deep digs. On undulating ground it would be necessary to lay a deep pipe through a hill to drain a depression at the other side of it. Now, with the Priestman Beavers, digging the trench down to 8 or 10 feet was not a problem. There was, however, a safety issue with trenches of that depth. In firm continuous clay the trench sides were reasonably stable and we had laid drains to 6 feet deep without shuttering at all.

What a deep trench can look like next day without shuttering.

The problems came with pockets of sand, which may or may not contain water. The sand would collapse into the trench, to be followed by the clay from above. The conventional form of shuttering consisting of timber vertical planks with cross-members hammered in-between them was a time-consuming business and made the trench difficult to work in. We built a steel cage, which fitted in the trench and allowed a man to work in it. It was built of angle iron, about 30 inches wide, with steel sheets on the side. It was 6 feet deep by 8 feet long.

With the cage 6 feet deep and Phil Bainbridge standing on it, his head is still below ground level, suggesting that the drain at that point was 12 to 14 feet deep.

On this occasion, the Priestman had first gone along digging 5 feet deep by the width of his tracks, and then gone along again in this track digging the trench. The Track Marshall needed to be on-hand to push the spoil away from the trench.

The 1969 Track Marshall.

A man could work safely in this cage levelling the trench bottom. The top was open so that a man on the surface could pass pipes down to the man in the cage. After he had laid pipes through the cage and the digger had dug the next length there was a length of chain attached to the cage, the other end of which was picked up by a tooth on the digger bucket, and the cage was now slid along the trench floor.

A rare event: two Allens working together, the near one with the tile bogie in tow is from the home depot, with Robert Bainbridge driving. The far one is the Rillington, with Jeff Wilson driving, using tiles off a trailer. The Whitlock is in the distance, being used for digging insets.

Another view of the two trenchers working together.

Two of the Priestmans were normally on tile drainage, with two men laying the tiles. The trenchers very often had the same number of staff, occasionally four, and they were turning out more than double the output of the Priestmans. The problem for us, as always, was stones. The Allen trencher, as well as the normal 9-inch bucket line, could also be had with a 12-inch line. A machine with the larger buckets was known to be better able to dig stones out, and we could not see any major disadvantages to the wider trench. There were hardly any schemes in the early 1970s needing permeable fill, particularly in the stony areas, which was the original reason for a narrow trench. Not all the work that the Priestmans were doing was excessively stony and the Priestmans were still going to be available for extreme conditions. So the decision was made, and for January 1971, a new trencher was bought with a 12-inch bucket line. Again, it was a Mark IVA, still with the Ford 75 horsepower engine.

The Whitlock 205 digger was sold in part exchange for the new trencher. Les Helme, who had driven the Whitlock from new and the Massey Ferguson before that, moved onto one of the Beavers, which was now reunited with its hydraulic jib. Raymond Anderson, Jim and Barry Chapman – the men who had worked with that Beaver – now manned the new trencher.

The new trencher worked well in the stony conditions and they achieved an acceptable work rate. They were not equipped with a Foster digger, as the other two gangs had been, as their need for a digger was greater because of the large stones that the trencher couldn't deal with. So a second-hand Ford 13/6 digger/loader combination was bought to accompany the new trencher.

The Ministry of Agriculture was still paying grants of 50 per cent on all drainage and ditching work, and in some cases, more than that. Some of the 'less favoured' areas could attract 60 per cent, and during the 1970s the government brought in the Farm and Horticultural Development Scheme. Under this scheme there were certain criteria that had to be met, such as record-keeping, agreeing a development plan and then sticking to it. But if all this was met they would pay an additional 10 per cent on all capital expenditure. So on tractors and machinery there was 10 per cent on buildings, which already qualified for 30 per cent. This was increased to 40 per cent, and the 50 per cent on land drainage was increased to 60 per cent.

There were some rather large contracts undertaken in the early seventies. One such job was the realigning of Brompton Beck, near Northallerton. The beck in its original form had some fairly aggressive meanders. It was dammed up to hold the water back while the new straight channel was dug. The Track Marshall then went into the beck, removed the dam and allowed the water to flow again.

The new channel for Brompton Beck, the Track Marshall being used to spread and level the spoil on both sides.

The Track Marshall 90 in the water, with Denis Cloughton at the controls, removing the dam and releasing the water.

The mood of the country was, as it had been since the war, focused on increasing production. The concept of overproduction and the need to cut back on production had not entered anybody's thinking. Consequently, all drainage contractors had full order books, which in our case meant that those three trenchers were fully occupied and working overtime. The two Beavers were fully employed on ditch cleaning and the old Priestman Wolf was used for occasional trenching work.

In the summer of 1972, we decided to replace the 1967 trencher with a new one. This was another Allen Mark IVA with 9-inch bucket line and the same 75 horsepower Ford power source. That deal was done through Caleys, of Burton Pidsea near Hull, with whom we had been dealing for all the Mark IV Allens. It was delivered in September and put straight to work. The work programme was colossal, particularly for the trenchers. Although the new machine had been delivered and put to work, the old machine had not been collected and was still in our yard. W.O. had discussions with Peter Caley and a deal was done for us to buy our old trencher back again. A makeshift gang was put together, which included Jim Akers with one of the Beavers and two local farmers' sons on a part-time basis.

Now we had four Allen trenchers in full-time work, one Priestman Beaver in full-time work, the other Beaver and the Wolf in occasional work and the Track Marshall fully occupied. On the general contracting there was one man driving a Hydrocut hedge cutter, and two others who switched to drainage work when the farm work was quiet. We were a workforce of 25 men. Mother worked full-time in the office and she had another woman in there on a part-time basis. W.O. was working full-time on prospective work and estimating for that work. He now covered an area stretching from the Pennines in the west to the east coast, from Scarborough to Redcar, and in 1972 he treated himself to a Range Rover. My brother, Donald, was full-time on supervision, which included the workshop and all the drainage sites.

Undrained land is not only unsuitable for arable cropping but also makes poor grazing land.

Postscript

I had bought a 60-acre farm in 1967. I was still employed by the family business, and relied on their machinery to do my farm work. I increasingly needed to spend more time on the farm and at some point in the late 1960s became self-employed. I ran the general contracting side of the business and from time to time still got involved with drainage work. In 1972, I rented an additional 70 acres of land and decided the time had come for me to own my own machinery and stand on my own two feet. We agreed to my purchasing three tractors, one combine, one baler, two trailers, plough, rotavator and corn drill.

Although I left the family firm at that point, drainage work, and the need for drainage, continued. Contractors continued and adopted new techniques as they came along. The last few rope-operated excavators soon disappeared, to be replaced by hydraulic machines of all sizes. Trenchers of the chain digging type were soon replacing the wheel diggers. Plastic pipe, after an unsure start, became accepted by the late 1970s, and in early 1980s was universally used. Grading with Laser beam also came into use, not only on trenchers but also when pipes were being laid by hand.

During the 1970s, farm crop yields were steadily increasing, with better crop protection products and increased use of fertilisers, not forgetting better soil structure as a result of all this drainage work. All this was to lead to a different mood sweeping across the nation and, indeed, across the whole of Europe. We were now members of the European Economic Community, or the Common Market as it was known, and all food supplies seemed to be in surplus. There were 'mountains' of butter, wheat and beef, 'lakes' of milk and wine, and the attitude of governments changed. They gradually moved to a position where there was to be no more support to increase food production, and the emphasis changed to protecting wildlife and its habitats.

One of the first things to go was the drainage grants. The land drainage offices within the Ministry of Agriculture were closed down and the remaining ADOs made redundant. Then all the thousands of final record plans, meticulously drawn on tracing linen to last a hundred years, were incinerated. Agricultural drainage done by the contractors fell away dramatically. That's not to say that the need for drainage fell away. In fact, there was and still is a vast acreage of land that would benefit from drainage.

Farmers are now being asked to reverse all the work that was done in the 1960s and early 1970s, the vast majority with grant aid: scrub clearance, grubbing-out of unwanted hedgerows and trees, draining and filling-in of old ponds, plus thousands of acres of land drainage, all under the heading of land improvement. They are now encouraged to create or restore wildlife habitat, wetlands and beetle banks as well as planting new hedgerows and trees. We have lived through a period where farmers were paid not to crop land, a scheme that was known as set-aside. When there were people in Africa starving to death, this must have been one of the most immoral acts of all time.

One thing that is certain is that the world population will continue to grow. Vast tracts of good agricultural land are lost each year to urban sprawl and road-building programmes, and farm output cannot go on increasing at the same rate as it did in the first 30 post-war years. The point must surely come when governments will have to change course yet again. In the mid-nineteenth and twentieth centuries, governments were forced to adopt panic measures to increase home produced foodstuffs, with programmes of land drainage and improvement. Could the same happen in the mid-twenty-first century?